Essential Maths 8 Core

Homework Book

Elmwood Education

First published 2021 by
Elmwood Education Limited
Unit 5 Mallow Park
Watchmead
Welwyn Garden City
AL7 1GX
Tel. 01707 333232

ISBN 9781 906 622 824

Books and magazines are protected by copyright, but UK schools have a **Licence to Copy** one chapter or 5%. Find out what's covered at cla.co.uk/licencetocopy

CCLA Copyright Licensing Agency

Typeset and illustrated by Tech-Set Ltd., Gateshead, Tyne and Wear.

CONTENTS

UNIT 5

UNIT 6

UNIT 1

1.1 Rules of indices

1 Work out

    a 2^3 **b** 3^3 **c** 8^3 **d** 1^3 **e** 20^3

2 Which is larger: 4^5 or 5^4 ?

3 Write down the calculations below which give an answer greater than 200

    a $5^3 + 4^2$ **b** $3^4 + 6^3$

    c $2^8 - 1^7$ **d** $10^3 - 9^3$

4 Which is larger and by how much? 2^6 or $56 + 3^2$

5 Each empty box below needs to contain a square number to make the calculation work. Write down each square number.

    a $4^3 + 5^2 - \square = 80$ **b** $\dfrac{10^3}{10^2} + \square = 35$

    c $6^3 - \square = 200$ **d** $2^7 - 7^2 - \square = 30$

6 '5 to the power of 5 is 3125.' True or false?

7 Work out, without a calculator.

    a 12^2 **b** $\left(\dfrac{1}{4}\right)^2$ **c** 10^4 **d** 0.4^2 **e** 0.1^3

8 Work out the difference between $4^4 + 3^5 + 2^8$ and 9^3

1 Answer 'true' or 'false'.

    a $7^2 \times 7^3 = 7^6$ **b** $5^{10} \div 5^3 = 5^7$ **c** $8 \times 8^5 = 64^5$

    d $\dfrac{3^7}{3^4} = 3^3$ **e** $\dfrac{7^7 \times 7}{7^4} = 7^2$ **f** $3^2 \times 3^2 = 9^4$

2 Work out and write each answer as a number in index form.

a $7^8 \div 7^5$ 　　　b 8×8 　　　c $2^3 \times 2^5 \times 2^2$

d $5^{10} \div 5^5$ 　　　e $\dfrac{2^{10}}{2^6}$ 　　　f $9 \times 9^4 \times 9$

g $\dfrac{11^6}{11^4}$ 　　　h $\dfrac{3^5 \times 3^4}{3^3}$ 　　　i $\dfrac{2 \times 2^4}{2^3}$

j $\dfrac{7^8 \times 7^4}{7^5 \times 7^2}$ 　　　k $\dfrac{5^4 \times 5^2 \times 5^2}{5^3 \times 5}$ 　　　l $\dfrac{6 \times 6^6 \times 6^3}{6^2 \times 6^2 \times 6^2}$

3 Which gives the greater answer?
Give reasons for your answer.

$A \boxed{5^3 \times 5}$ 　or　 $B \boxed{\dfrac{5^8}{5^4}}$

4 Copy and complete

a $\boxed{} \times 3^6 = 3^8$ 　　　b $5^3 \times \boxed{} = 5^9$ 　　　c $2^8 \div \boxed{} = 2^5$

d $\dfrac{\boxed{}}{7^4} = 7^2$ 　　　e $\boxed{} \div 3^5 = 3^2$ 　　　f $\dfrac{9^4 \times \boxed{}}{9^3 \times 9^3} = 9^3$

5 Elsie says that $3^2 \times 3^2 \times 3^2 = 3^8$. Is she correct? Give a clear reason for your answer.

6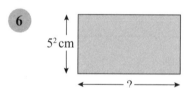

The area of this rectangle is $5^5\,\text{cm}^2$
Write down the length of the missing side in index form.

7 In this question, give each answer as an ordinary number.
For example, $7^5 \div 7^3 = 7^2 = 7 \times 7 = 49$

a $3^2 \times 3^2$ 　　　b $5^2 \times 5$ 　　　c $7^8 \div 7^7$

d $\dfrac{3^4 \times 3^2}{3^3}$ 　　　e $\dfrac{5^6 \times 5^4}{5^5 \times 5^5}$ 　　　f $2^2 \times 2^2 \times 2^3$

8 Which rectangle has the greater area and by how much?

Give the answer as an ordinary number.

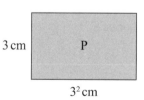

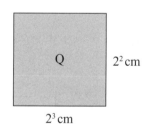

1.2 Prime factors, HCF and LCM

1 Which number below is *not* a factor of 40?

| 20 | 8 | 4 | 5 | 6 | 10 |

2 Write down all the prime numbers between 10 and 20

3 Which numbers below are multiples of 7?

35   77   21   39   51   42

4 'The sum of all the prime numbers less than 8 is 17.' True or false?

5 Write down two prime numbers which add up to 28

6 Write down all the factors of 32

7 Three factors of 20 add up to 16. Write down two different ways in which this can be done.

8 **a** List all the factors of 30

 b List all the factors of 48

 c Write down the highest common factor of 30 and 48

9 Copy and fill in the empty boxes for this sequence.

| 1 | 3 | 6 | 10 | | 21 | | | 45 |

10 **a** Write down the first six multiples of 15

 b Write down the first six multiples of 20

 c Write down the lowest common multiple of 15 and 20

11

True story?
A dog had to have 13 golf balls
removed from his stomach after
eating them during walks.
Oscar, a black labrador, was
taken to the vet after his
owner noticed a rattling noise
coming from his pet's stomach.
The dog needed no stitches
after the operation and is now
said to be in good health!

If the dog had eaten golf balls equivalent
to the next highest prime number, how
many golf balls would have been removed
from his stomach?

12 Find the lowest common multiple of 18 and 30

13 Find the highest common factor of 28 and 63

14 Why can a prime number *not* have 0 as its last digit?

15 A baker delivers to a village every 5 days. A butcher delivers to the village every 7 days. How often will the baker and butcher deliver on the same day?

HWK 2M ——————————————————————————————— **Main Book page 11**

1 Copy and complete this factor tree.

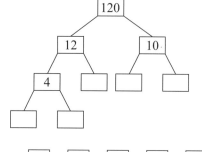

$$120 = \Box \times \Box \times \Box \times \Box \times \Box$$

2 Draw factor trees for the following numbers.

    a 50   **b** 140   **c** 240   **d** 420

3 A factor tree for 693 is shown.

    a Explain clearly a mistake that has been made.

    b Express 693 as the product of its prime factors.

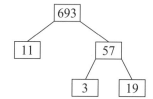

4 Find a number with prime factors of only 2, 7 and 13

5 Express 1820 as the product of its prime factors.

HWK 3M ——————————————————————————————— **Main Book page 12**

1 The prime factors of 42 and 910 are shown in the Venn diagram opposite.

    a Work out the HCF of 42 and 910

    b Work out the LCM of 42 and 910

42   910

3   2   5

7   13

2 198   63

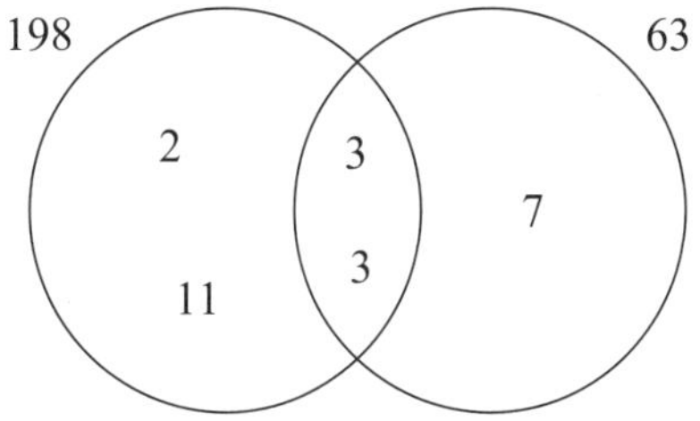

The prime factors of 198 and 63 are shown in the Venn diagram opposite.

2

3

7

3

11

a Work out the HCF of 63 and 198

b Work out the LCM of 63 and 198

3 **a** If $210 = 2 \times 3 \times 5 \times 7$ and $525 = 3 \times 5 \times 5 \times 7$, draw a Venn diagram for the prime factors of 210 and 525

    b Work out the HCF of 210 and 525

    c Work out the LCM of 210 and 525

4 **a** Draw factor trees then a Venn diagram for the prime factors of 630 and 1560

    b Find the HCF of 630 and 1560

    c Find the LCM of 630 and 1560

5 Draw factor trees and Venn diagrams to find the HCF and LCM of each pair of numbers below.

    a 105 and 110   **b** 231 and 273   **c** 195 and 260

6 Find the HCF and LCM of 770 and 1365

1.3 Using algebra

HWK 1M ———————————————————— **Main Book page 16**

1 Answer 'true' or 'false'.

    a $5m + 2m + 2n = 9mn$ **b** $5x + y + 3y = 5x + 4y$

    c $2p + 4 + 2p = 4p + 4$ **d** $4n - 2n + 3 = 5n$

Simplify the expressions in questions **2** to **10** by collecting like terms.

2 $3a + 4b + 2a$ **3** $8m + 3n + 4n - 4m$ **4** $2a + 5 + a + 1$

5 $4x + 3 - 2x - 1$ **6** $7w - 4w + 3 + 2w$ **7** $4m + 3m + 4n - 5m$

8 $7 + 4p - 3 - 3p$ **9** $5x - 2x + 6 - 5$ **10** $5a - a + 3 - 2a$

11 Find two matching pairs of expressions.

    A $\boxed{1 + 2m + 3}$ B $\boxed{2 + m + 4m - 1}$ C $\boxed{2 + 6m - 3m - 1}$

              D $\boxed{7m + 1 - 2m}$ E $\boxed{5m + 4 - 3m}$

12 Find an expression for the total distance from A to C.

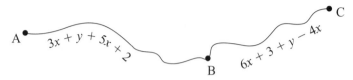

13 $5n^2 + 4n - n^2 = 5 + 4n$. Is this true or false?
Give a reason for your answer.

14 Simplify

a $4n^2 + 3n$ **b** $6y^2 - y^2 + 2y^2$ **c** $6m^2 + 5m - 2m$

d $3x^2 + 2x^2 + 4x$ **e** $p^2 + 4p - p + p^2$ **f** $4 + n^2 + 2n^2 - 1$

HWK 2M   **Main Book page 17**

1 Answer 'true' or 'false'.

a $4 + m = 4m$ **b** $n \div 3 = \dfrac{n}{3}$ **c** $5p - p = 5$

d $xy = yx$ **e** $m \times m = m^2$ **f** $4x + x = 5x$

g $a + b = ab$ **h** $\dfrac{6w}{3} = 2w$ **i** $a \times a \times a = a^3$

2 Here are some cards.

| $a + 3$ | $5a$ | a^2 |

| $a - 1$ | $a \div 2$ | $a \times a$ | $4a - a$ |

| $2a + a + a$ | $5 \div a$ | $4a$ |

a Which card is the same as $\boxed{a + a + a}$?

b Which card is the same as $\boxed{\dfrac{5}{a}}$?

c The card $\boxed{a \times a}$ is the same as the card $\boxed{a^2}$.

    Which other pair of cards are the same as each other?

d Which card is the same as $\boxed{\dfrac{1}{2}a}$?

e What is the difference in the value of the cards $\boxed{a + 3}$ and $\boxed{a - 1}$?

3 Tim has £$(5n + 7)$. He buys a shirt for £$(2n + 3)$. How much money does Tim now have?

4 Lily is running a $(9w + 8)$ metre race. Write down an expression for how many more metres Lily has to run if she has completed $(4w + 7)$ metres so far.

5 Simplify each expression.

a $5m \times 3n$ b $6a \times 9b$ c $3p \times 2q \times 6r$

d $y \times y$ e $3m \times 2m$ f $7n \times 4n$

g $3a \times 2b \times 8$ h $4y \times 6 \times 2y$ i $4n \times 3m \times 2n$

6 If $4a \times 2b \times 3c = 24abc$, write down a question which gives the answer $48abc$

HWK 3M	Main Book page 19

1 Here is a flow diagram for the expression $4(2n - 3)$

Find the expression for each of the following flow diagrams.

2 Draw the flow diagram for the following expressions.

a $6(4n + 1)$ b $4(5n - 8)$ c $5(n^2 + 4)$

d $\dfrac{3n - 6}{7}$ e $7(n - 4)^2$ f $8(n + 5)^2$

3 Write down an expression for each statement below.

a Start with n, add y and then multiply the result by 7

b Start with y, square it and then subtract p

c Start with h, double it, square the result and then add m

4 Melanie weighs 50 kg. During the next fortnight she loses m kg. How much does she weigh now?

5 Sid has £35. His mother gives him £x then Sid spends £y. How much money does Sid now have?

6 There are x chocolates in a box. Marie eats y chocolates and Pete eats 7 chocolates. How many chocolates are now in the box?

7 Will is paid £7 per hour. How much does he earn if he works for y hours?

8

8 A book costs £9 and a magazine costs £3.
Write down an expression for the total cost of *x* books and *y* magazines.

HWK 4M ————————————————— **Main Book page 21**

1 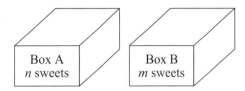 Ryan has two boxes of sweets, as shown.

Ryan takes five sweets out of box A and four sweets out of box B.

a How many sweets are left in box A?

b How many sweets are left in box B?

c What is the total number of sweets left in both boxes?

d Ryan now puts one sweet back into box B. How many sweets are now in box B?

2 Mark has £*n*. Marcus has three times as much money as Mark. Marcus spends £15.
How much money does Marcus now have?

3 In number walls each brick is made by
adding the two bricks underneath it.

Draw the walls below and fill in the missing expressions.

a

?
$a + b$	$a + b$

b

| ? |
| ? | ? |
| $m - n$ | $m + n$ | $2n$ |

c

| ? |
| ? | ? |
| $a + 2b$ | $a - b$ | a |

d

	$5a + 2b$	
$3a$	?
$2a + b$	?	?

e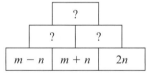

	$2a + 4b$	
?	a
?	?	$a - b$

f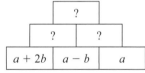

	$4c + d$	
$3c + d$	?
?	$2d$	?

4 Felix has £$(9n + 23)$. He spends £$(3n + 9)$. He gives half of the remaining money to his
sister. How much money does he have left?

5 A bottle of water costs £*x*. How much change from a £20 note will Gemma get if she buys
three bottles of water?

1.4 Construction and locus

You need a ruler, protractor and pair of compasses.

1 Construct triangle ABC as shown.
Use a protractor to measure AB̂C.

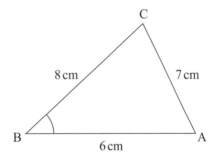

2 Construct each triangle and measure the side *x*.

a

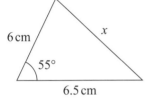

b

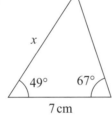

c

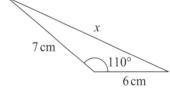

3 Construct rhombus PQRS as shown.
Use a protractor to measure PQ̂R.

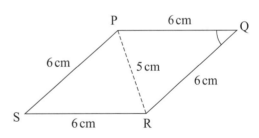

4

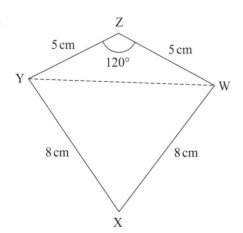

Construct the kite WXYZ.
Use a protractor to measure WX̂Y.

10

Remember: The *locus* of a point is the path traced out by the point as it moves.

1 Mark a point A with a cross. Hundreds of ants stand *exactly* 6 cm from the point A. Draw a diagram to show this.

2 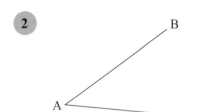 Copy this diagram. The ants now move so that each ant is *exactly* the same distance from line AB as line AC. Show this on your diagram.

3 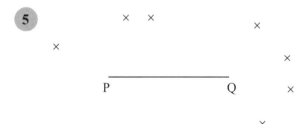 This diagram shows a white ball and a black ball on a snooker table. Copy the diagram. Darryl hits the white ball against the black ball. The black ball hits the side of the table at A then goes down the hole in the bottom right-hand corner. Darryl is very surprised. Show what happens to the black ball on your diagram.

4 Draw another copy of the snooker table with the black ball in the same starting position. If the black ball goes down a different hole, show what happens to the black ball on your diagram.
Describe what happens to the black ball and which hole it goes down.

5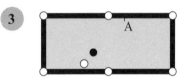
All the crosses shown above are 2.5 cm away from the line PQ.
Copy the diagram and draw the locus of *all* the points 2.5 cm away from the line PQ.

6 Shade the locus of all the points which are less than or equal to 3 cm from a fixed point P.

7 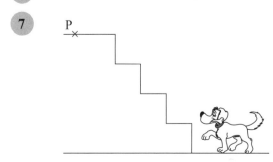 A dog with a bone in its mouth runs up these stairs and drops the bone on the point marked P.

Copy the stairs and draw a rough sketch of the locus of the bone as it travels from the bottom of the stairs to the point P.

You need a ruler, protractor and pair of compasses.

1   Draw a horizontal line PQ of length 7 cm. Construct the perpendicular bisector of PQ.

2   Draw an angle of 60°. Construct the bisector of the angle.

3   **a** Construct the perpendicular bisector of a line AB as shown.
          Label the bisector CD.
          Label the point Y as shown.

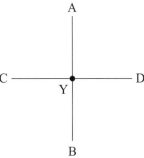

   b Construct the bisector of $A\widehat{Y}D$.

   c Construct the bisector of $B\widehat{Y}D$.

   d Label the bisectors as shown opposite.

   e Use your protractor to measure $C\widehat{Y}X$.

   f Use your protractor to measure $A\widehat{Y}Z$.

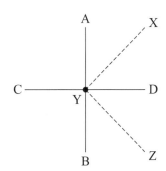

4   **a** Use a protractor to draw a 90° angle.

   b Use a ruler and compasses only to bisect
          this angle to make a 45° angle.

   c Use a ruler and compasses only to construct
          an angle of $22\frac{1}{2}°$

5   • A   Copy this diagram and construct the line which
                                 passes through A and is perpendicular to the line.

────────────────────────

6

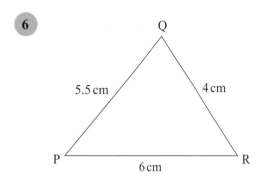

Q

5.5 cm   4 cm

P   6 cm   R

a Use a ruler and compasses only to construct triangle PQR as shown.

b Construct the angle bisector of QP̂R. Label this line PX.

c Construct the angle bisector of PR̂Q. Label this line RY.

d Use your protractor to measure QP̂X and PR̂Y.

1.5 Angles

Find the angles marked with letters.

1

68°
a   43°

2

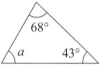

d
c
b
45°

3

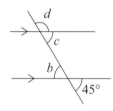

f
g
53°
e

4

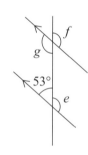

149°   164°
h

5

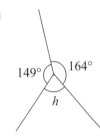

i   112° *j*
78°   *k*

6

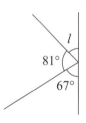

l
81°
67°

7

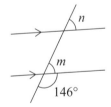

n
m
146°

8

134°
65°
p

9

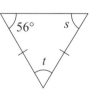

32°
q
r
25°

10

56°   *s*
t

11

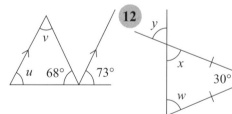

v
u 68° 73°

12

y
x
30°
w

13

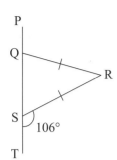

Work out the value of QR̂S by completing the answer below.

QŜR = 74°

(angles on a s_____ l_____ add up to _____°)

SQ̂R = _____

(base angles in an i_____ triangle are equal)

QR̂S = _____

(angles in a triangle add up to _____°)

14

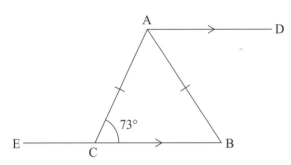

Work out the value of BÂD, giving reasons as shown in question **13**.

HWK 1E   Main Book page 38

---

1   Copy and complete this proof to show that AD̂C is equal to AB̂C in this kite.

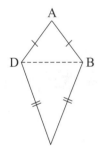

AD̂B = ☐ (angles in isosceles triangle ADB)

BD̂C = ☐ (angles in isosceles triangle BDC)

AD̂C = AD̂B + BD̂C

= ☐ + ☐

= AB̂C

2   Copy and complete this proof for the sum of the angles in a pentagon.

Draw any pentagon (5 sides) as shown.

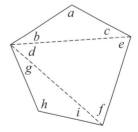

$a + $ ☐ $+ c = 180°$ (angles in a △)

$d + e + f = $ ☐ (angles in a △)

$g + $ ☐ $+ $ ☐ $= $ ☐ (angles in a △)

We must have

$a + $ ☐ $+ c + d + e + f + g + $ ☐ $+ $ ☐ $= $ ☐

This shows that the sum of the angles in a pentagon is ☐ .

14

3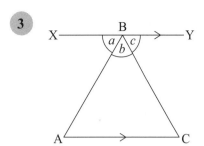

$a + b + c = 180°$ (angles on a straight line).
Prove that the sum of the angles in a triangle is 180°

4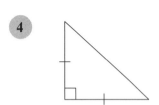

Prove that the angles in a right-angled isosceles triangle
are 90°, 45° and 45°

5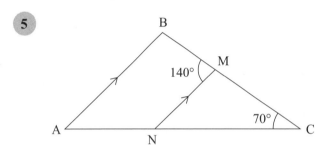

Prove that triangle ABC is isosceles.

Find the angles marked with letters.

1 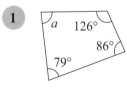   **2**    **3** 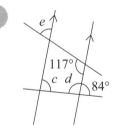   **4**

5 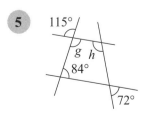   **6** 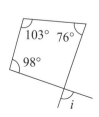   **7**    **8**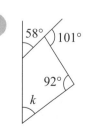

9 Explain why the angles shown opposite are not possible.

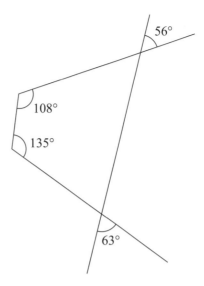

10 Find the value of each angle shown below, giving full reasons for each answer.

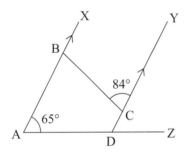

a AB̂C   **b** BĈD

c AD̂C   **d** CD̂Z

HWK 3M	**Main Book page 41**

Find the angles marked with letters.

1
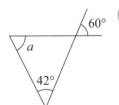

2

3
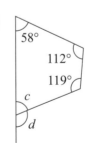

4
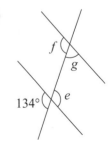

16

5

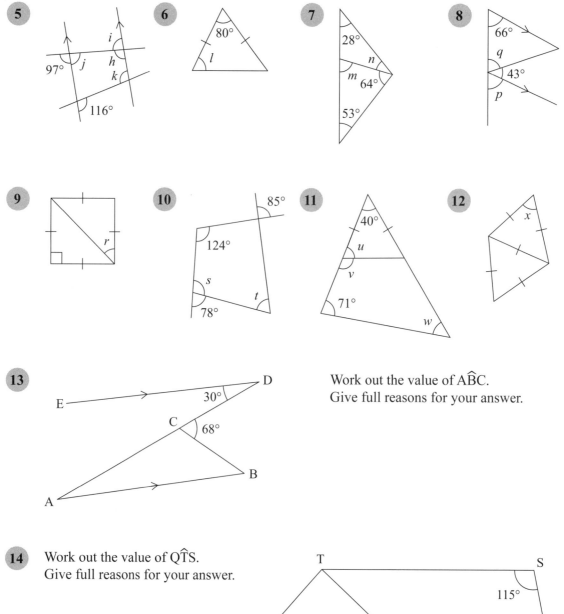

i

j *h*

97° *k*

116°

6

80°

l

7

28°

n

m 64°

53°

8

66°

q

43°

p

9

r

10

85°

124°

s

78° *t*

11

40°

u

v

71°

w

12

x

13

E

D

30°

C

68°

B

A

Work out the value of AB̂C.
Give full reasons for your answer.

14 Work out the value of QT̂S.
Give full reasons for your answer.

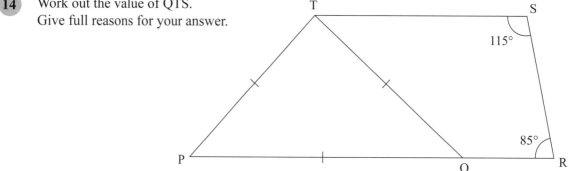

T

S

115°

85°

P

Q

R

1.6 Fractions

1   Write the shaded areas as both mixed numbers and improper fractions.

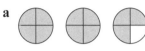

2   Change these improper fractions to mixed numbers or whole numbers only.

a $\dfrac{7}{2}$ **b** $\dfrac{13}{3}$ **c** $\dfrac{14}{5}$ **d** $\dfrac{13}{4}$ **e** $\dfrac{23}{7}$

f $\dfrac{11}{6}$ **g** $\dfrac{33}{10}$ **h** $\dfrac{21}{8}$ **i** $\dfrac{15}{7}$ **j** $\dfrac{29}{5}$

3   Change these mixed numbers to improper fractions.

a $4\dfrac{2}{3}$ **b** $2\dfrac{1}{4}$ **c** $5\dfrac{3}{4}$ **d** $7\dfrac{1}{2}$ **e** $3\dfrac{4}{5}$

f $5\dfrac{3}{8}$ **g** $2\dfrac{7}{9}$ **h** $6\dfrac{1}{6}$ **i** $4\dfrac{2}{5}$ **j** $5\dfrac{7}{10}$

4   Match up the improper fractions to the mixed numbers (beware: there is one odd one out).

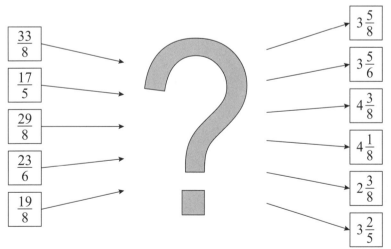

5   How many eighths are there in $6\dfrac{5}{8}$?

6   Which is greater: the number of fifths in $4\dfrac{4}{5}$ or the number of sevenths in $3\dfrac{4}{7}$?

18

1 Which fraction is *not* equivalent to the others?

$\left(\dfrac{12}{15}\right)$ $\left(\dfrac{20}{25}\right)$ $\left(\dfrac{8}{10}\right)$ $\left(\dfrac{32}{40}\right)$ $\left(\dfrac{25}{30}\right)$ $\left(\dfrac{24}{30}\right)$

2 Answer 'true' or 'false'.

a $\dfrac{18}{24} = \dfrac{3}{4}$ **b** $\dfrac{7}{8} = \dfrac{24}{32}$ **c** $\dfrac{5}{9} = \dfrac{20}{36}$

d $\dfrac{24}{28} = \dfrac{6}{7}$ **e** $\dfrac{30}{42} = \dfrac{4}{7}$ **f** $\dfrac{3}{10} = \dfrac{21}{70}$

3 Work out

a $\dfrac{3}{5} - \dfrac{1}{3}$ **b** $\dfrac{1}{4} + \dfrac{2}{3}$ **c** $\dfrac{2}{5} + \dfrac{3}{8}$ **d** $\dfrac{5}{7} - \dfrac{1}{8}$

e $\dfrac{1}{2} - \dfrac{3}{7}$ **f** $\dfrac{2}{9} + \dfrac{3}{10}$ **g** $\dfrac{7}{8} - \dfrac{2}{3}$ **h** $\dfrac{9}{10} - \dfrac{5}{7}$

4 Louise and Jake are sharing a pizza. Louise eats $\dfrac{2}{5}$ of the pizza and Jake eats $\dfrac{3}{7}$ of the pizza. What fraction of the pizza is left?

5 Ben carpets $\dfrac{5}{8}$ of his new house. He uses wood flooring for $\dfrac{1}{4}$ of the house.

The remaining floor area in his house is tiled. What fraction of the floor area is tiled?

6 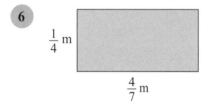 Work out the perimeter of this rectangle.

$\dfrac{1}{4}$ m

$\dfrac{4}{7}$ m

7 A test has four parts.
This table shows what fraction
of the test each part is.

Part A	Part B	Part C	Part D
$\dfrac{1}{3}$	$\dfrac{1}{5}$	$\dfrac{1}{4}$	?

a What fraction of the test is part D?

b Janice has completed parts A and B. What fraction of the test has she still got to do?

8 Sid ate $\dfrac{1}{3}$ of a birthday cake then ate another $\dfrac{1}{5}$. Danielle ate $\dfrac{3}{10}$ of the cake then ate

another $\dfrac{1}{20}$. What fraction more of the cake did Sid eat compared with Danielle?

1 Copy and complete

$$2\frac{1}{2} + 1\frac{3}{5} = \frac{5}{2} + \frac{8}{5} = \frac{\square}{10} + \frac{\square}{10} = \frac{\square}{10} = 4\frac{\square}{10}$$

2 Work out, leaving each answer as a mixed number.

a $1\frac{1}{4} + 1\frac{1}{3}$ **b** $3\frac{1}{2} + 2\frac{1}{3}$ **c** $4\frac{3}{4} - 3\frac{1}{3}$

d $2\frac{1}{3} - \frac{5}{8}$ **e** $1\frac{1}{3} + 2\frac{5}{6}$ **f** $4\frac{1}{2} - 2\frac{7}{8}$

3 The distance from Alwich to Hinton is $3\frac{2}{5}$ miles.

How far is it from Boxley to Hinton?

4 $4\frac{1}{2} - \square = 2\frac{2}{3}$ What is the missing number?

5 Work out the perimeter of this triangle.

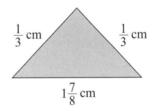

1 Work out

a $\frac{3}{4}$ of 24 **b** $\frac{2}{3}$ of 36 **c** $\frac{7}{10}$ of 80 **d** $\frac{5}{6}$ of 30

e $\frac{2}{5}$ of 45 **f** $\frac{3}{7}$ of 35 **g** $\frac{3}{20}$ of 140 **h** $\frac{4}{9}$ of 54

2 A tin of biscuits has 32 biscuits when full.
How many biscuits are there when the tin is only $\frac{3}{8}$ full?

3 Work out each question below. Cancel down the answers if possible.

a $\frac{1}{8} \times \frac{4}{5}$ **b** $\frac{2}{3} \times \frac{6}{7}$ **c** $\frac{3}{10} \times \frac{5}{6}$ **d** $\frac{5}{7} \times \frac{1}{10}$

e $\frac{4}{7} \times \frac{7}{8}$ **f** $\frac{9}{10} \times \frac{5}{12}$ **g** $\frac{5}{9} \times \frac{6}{7}$ **h** $\frac{7}{12} \times \frac{6}{11}$

4 Martin has to travel 16 km back to his village. He runs $\frac{3}{8}$ of the journey, then walks $\frac{3}{5}$ of the remaining distance. How far is he now from his village?

5 Copy and complete.

a $\frac{\square}{3}$ of 15 = 10

b $\frac{\square}{8}$ of 24 = 21

c $\frac{5}{\square}$ of 18 = 15

6

$\frac{2}{3}$ m | A |

$\frac{9}{10}$ m

Which rectangle has the larger area and by how much?

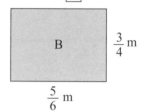

B $\frac{3}{4}$ m

$\frac{5}{6}$ m

7 Answer 'true' or 'false'.

a $\frac{3}{8} \times 4 = \frac{12}{32}$

b $\frac{2}{3} \times 6 = 4$

c $\frac{1}{6} \times 4 = \frac{2}{3}$

d $\frac{3}{4} \times 2 = \frac{6}{8}$

HWK 5M | **Main Book page 53**

1 Work out   **a** $2\frac{3}{4} \times \frac{8}{9}$ **b** $3\frac{1}{3} \times \frac{2}{5}$

2 Work out

a $2\frac{1}{3} \times \frac{1}{2}$

b $3\frac{1}{2} \times 1\frac{1}{4}$

c $2\frac{3}{4} \times 2\frac{3}{4}$

d $1\frac{2}{3} \times 1\frac{1}{2}$

3

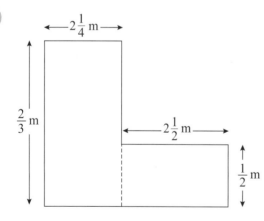

Work out the total area of this shape.

4 Find the missing fraction.

$\dfrac{\square}{\square} \div 2\frac{1}{2} = 1\frac{1}{3}$

5 Work out $\left(1\frac{2}{3} \times \frac{7}{10}\right) - \left(\frac{3}{4} \times \frac{2}{9}\right)$

1   **a** How many fifths are there in 4?

     b How many thirds are there in 7?

     c How many sixths are there in 8?

2   Work out

     a $6 \div \dfrac{1}{4}$ **b** $9 \div \dfrac{1}{7}$ **c** $3 \div \dfrac{1}{10}$ **d** $4 \div \dfrac{1}{9}$ **e** $10 \div \dfrac{1}{20}$ **f** $8 \div \dfrac{1}{50}$

3   Copy and complete

     a $\square \div \dfrac{1}{8} = 32$ **b** $\square \div \dfrac{1}{6} = 54$ **c** $9 \div \dfrac{\square}{\square} = 45$

4   Copy and complete each number chain.

     a $\boxed{} \xrightarrow{\div \frac{1}{3}} \boxed{24} \xrightarrow{\div \frac{1}{2}} \boxed{}$

     b $\boxed{} \xrightarrow{\div \frac{1}{5}} \boxed{} \xrightarrow{\div \frac{1}{6}} \boxed{} \xrightarrow{\div \frac{1}{4}} \boxed{120}$

     c $\boxed{} \xrightarrow{\times \frac{1}{6}} \boxed{} \xrightarrow{\div \frac{1}{5}} \boxed{} \xrightarrow{\times \frac{1}{10}} \boxed{4}$

5   Work out $3 \div \dfrac{1}{5} \div \dfrac{1}{3}$

1   Copy and complete

     $\dfrac{2}{3} \div \dfrac{9}{11} = \dfrac{2}{3} \times \dfrac{11}{\square} = \dfrac{22}{\square}$

2   Work out

     a $\dfrac{1}{4} \div \dfrac{1}{3}$ **b** $\dfrac{1}{2} \div \dfrac{3}{4}$ **c** $\dfrac{3}{8} \div \dfrac{1}{2}$ **d** $\dfrac{2}{5} \div \dfrac{7}{10}$

     e $\dfrac{3}{5} \div \dfrac{7}{8}$ **f** $\dfrac{1}{9} \div \dfrac{2}{3}$ **g** $\dfrac{4}{7} \div \dfrac{7}{8}$ **h** $\dfrac{7}{12} \div \dfrac{3}{4}$

3   Sam is watching his weight. He allows himself $\dfrac{3}{40}$ of a box of cereal for his breakfast, which he measures out carefully.

     How many breakfasts will he get from six boxes of cereal?

4 Work out

a $2\frac{1}{2} \div \frac{3}{7}$ **b** $1\frac{2}{3} \div \frac{5}{8}$ **c** $2\frac{1}{4} \div 3\frac{1}{2}$

5

×		$\frac{2}{5}$	
		$\frac{1}{20}$	
$\frac{1}{2}$	$\frac{3}{5}$		
$\frac{7}{10}$			$2\frac{1}{3}$

Copy and complete this multiplication table.

1.7 Probability 1

HWK 1M ───────────────────────────────── **Main Book page 59**

1 With this spinner find the probability of getting

a a 5 **b** a multiple of 4

c a prime number **d** not an even number.

2 The probability of Sid's dog barking sometime in the morning is 0.97.
What is the probability of Sid's dog not barking sometime in the morning?

3 A dice is thrown. What is the probability of getting

a a 3 **b** a number less than 5 **c** a square number?

4

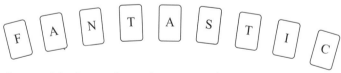

One card is chosen from above at random.

Find the probability of getting

a an 'S' **b** not a 'T' **c** a vowel.

5 47% of the children in Year 8 in Colne Community School are boys.
When Year 8 walk into an assembly, what is the probability that the first child to arrive will
be a girl?

6 A pack of cards has 13 clubs, 13 diamonds, 13 hearts and 13 spades.

One card is selected at random from the pack.

Find the probability of selecting

a a heart **b** not a club.

7 Rosa is playing pool and pots 5 balls in a row. Colm says that Rosa will definitely pot the next ball. Is Colm correct? Justify your answer.

8 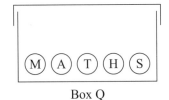 Two boxes contain discs as shown.

Box P   Box Q

a One disc is removed from box P. What is the probability of selecting a vowel? The disc is placed back in box P.

b Four more discs, Ⓥ Ⓔ Ⓡ Ⓨ, are added to box P. If one disc is now removed from box P, what is the probability of selecting a vowel? The disc is placed back in box P.

c The disc Ⓐ is now taken out of box Q and placed in box P. If one disc is now removed from box P, what is the probability of selecting a vowel?

9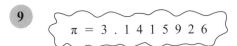

One digit is chosen at random from the digits shown above.

What is the probability of selecting

a the digit '1' **b** a digit which is not a prime number?

10 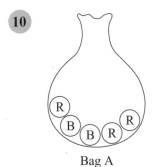 Two bags have red (R) and black (B) balls in them as shown.

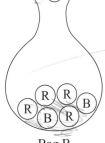

Bag A   Bag B

a Find the probability of selecting a black ball from bag A.

b A black ball is taken from bag A and put into bag B. A ball is then selected at random from bag B. What is the probability that this ball is not a black ball?

HWK 2M ──────────────────────────────── **Main Book page 61**

1 A bag contains yellow and red balls as shown.
One ball is selected at random from the bag and
then replaced. This is done 420 times.
How many times would you expect to select

   a a red ball   **b** a yellow ball?

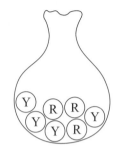

2 A fair dice is rolled 390 times. How many times would you expect to roll a multiple of 3?

3 The probability of it raining on any one day at Carnwell beach is $\frac{1}{3}$. On how many days
would you expect it *not* to rain during a three-week holiday at Carnwell beach?

4 Four out of every seven students in Year 8 are girls. 42 students from Year 8 are in the main
school hall. How many of these students would you expect to be girls?

5 Two out of every nine trains are late at Henton station. How many trains would you expect to
be on time out of the next 54 trains to arrive at Henton station?

6 A coin is biased so that the probability of throwing 'tails' is 0.63. How many 'heads' would
you expect when the coin is thrown 500 times?

7 Will has the Jack, Queen, King, Ace of Clubs and the Ace of Hearts. Amy chooses one of his
cards and then Mark chooses one of Will's cards.

   a If Amy chooses an Ace, what is the probability of Mark also choosing an Ace?

   b If Amy chooses a King, what is the probability of Mark choosing an Ace?

8 The probability of picking the winner of a horse race is 0.4.
How many winners would you expect to pick for the next 45 races?

9 A large box contains 4 blue footballs and 5 yellow footballs. For each sports lesson, one
football is randomly chosen then put back in the box at the end of the lesson. How many
times would you expect a yellow football to be chosen in the next 36 sports lessons?

10 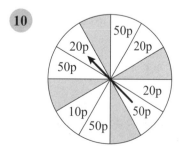 At a school fête a person pays 30p to spin the pointer opposite.
The person wins the amount shown by the pointer.
The game is played 480 times.
What profit would the school expect to make?

1 A bag contains some discs. Each disc has one of three letters on it – 'T', 'R' or 'Y'.
Jan randomly takes a disc from the bag and then replaces it.
She does this 80 times and records the results.

Letter	T	R	Y
Frequency	23	34	23

Use the results shown to estimate the probability that the next disc she takes out will be

a a 'Y' **b** an 'R'.

2 Lara rolls a fair dice 120 times. Each time she records the number it lands on.

Number	1	2	3	4	5	6
Frequency	22	25	4	23	27	19

a What seems 'strange' about these results?

b How many times would you have expected the dice to land on each different number?

c If Lara rolled the dice another 120 times, would you expect her to get the same results?

3 Chad and Marie throw a shoe to see if it will land on its heel or not. Chad throws 50 times
and Marie throws 130 times. The results are shown below.

Chad
Throws	50
Heel landings	28

Marie
Throws	130
Heel landings	57

The shoe is thrown again.

a For Chad, what is the probability of the shoe landing on its heel?

b For Marie, what is the probability of the shoe landing on its heel?

c Which probability is likely to be more reliable?
Give a reason for your answer.

d If you put Chad's and Marie's results together, what is the probability of the shoe landing
on its heel if it is thrown again?

e Based on Chad's and Marie's combined results, how many times would you expect the
shoe to land on its heel if it is thrown 360 times?

4 How many tails would you expect to get if you toss a coin 50 times?
Toss a coin 50 times. Write down how your results compare with what you expected to get.

UNIT 2

2.1 Percentages 1

1 1000 people were asked if they were connected to the internet at home. 850 people said 'yes'. What percentage of the people said 'yes'?

2 Hatton United played 50 football games. They drew 9 games and lost 10 games. What percentage of the games did Hatton United win?

3 Martin was absent from school for 14 out of 200 days. For what percentage of the days did Martin go to school?

4 Four people obtain the test marks shown below.

Jane	Tobias	Hal	Meg
$\frac{11}{20}$	$\frac{20}{40}$	$\frac{108}{200}$	$\frac{13}{25}$

    a Change each mark to a percentage and write down each name in order of the percentage scored, starting with the highest.

    b Meg scored a higher percentage than Tobias. How much more did she score?

5 Nina has to wash the evening dishes on four of the five weekdays. On what percentage of the weekdays does she *not* have to wash the evening dishes?

6 Matt has £60. He spends one third of his money on a shirt. He then sees a pair of trousers for £30. What percentage of his remaining money would he use if he buys the trousers?

7 Yasmin has 40 pairs of shoes. If 8 pairs of shoes are red, what percentage of her shoes are *not* red?

8 7 out of 9 people in Oak Street own a car. 5 out of 11 people in Elm Street own a car. What percentage of the people in both streets own a car?

9 The 'Magna' store on the high street sells electrical goods. 25 people visit the store on Saturday and 8 of them buy something. On the same day, 500 people visit the online store and 140 of them buy something.

    a What percentage of people visiting the store on the high street buy something?

    b What percentage of people visiting the online store buy something?

    c What is the percentage difference between people buying something in the store compared with people buying online?

You may use a calculator. Give all answers to one decimal place.

1 8 people out of 15 in a rugby team are more than 6 feet tall. What percentage of the team are more than 6 feet tall?

2   What percentage of these faces are 'smiley'?

3 17 out of 163 people said that Indian food was their favourite food. What percentage of the people was this?

4 A 150 g chocolate bar contains 59 g fat and 12 g fibre. What percentage of the chocolate bar is *neither* fat nor fibre?

5 The table shows how many children wear glasses in Year 8 at Denton High School.

   a What percentage of the girls wear glasses?

   b What percentage of all the children do not wear glasses?

	Boys	Girls	Total
Wear glasses	17	28	45
Do not wear glasses	74	102	176
Total	91	130	221

6 Three basketball players are shooting baskets. Their success rate is shown opposite.

   a Who had the highest percentage rate of success?

   b What is the percentage difference in the success rates of Cheryl and Mike?

	Successes	Total attempts
Jason	39	143
Cheryl	48	170
Mike	27	71

7

	Men	Women	Total
Under 21	174	263	437
21 to 65	320	419	739
Over 65	211	306	517
Total	705	988	1693

One day a supermarket records the ages of the shoppers. The results are shown in the table.

a What percentage of the men were over 65?

b What percentage of the people were 21 to 65 years old?

c What percentage of the women were 65 or *under* 65 years old?

Do not use a calculator.

1 Answer 'true' or 'false'.

  a 5% of £60 = £20 **b** 30% of £40 = £12 **c** 80% of £70 = £56

  d 20% of £320 = £64 **e** 5% of £140 = £28 **f** 60% of £90 = £54

2 Neil has a house worth £340 000. Two years later its value has gone down by 20%. How much money has its value gone down by?

3 Find the odd one out.

  (30% of £30)   (5% of £160)   (40% of £20)

4 Which is larger?   (3% of £600) or (4% of £500)

5 Work out

  a 2% of £5400 **b** 13% of £600 **c** 11% of £800

6 Marvin is trying to sell his car for £2500. He is not having much luck so decides to knock 20% off the selling price. How much is he asking for his car now?

7 The cost of a £560 TV is increased by 5%. What is the new cost of the TV?

8 A farmer keeps 60 goats. During the next two years the number of goats increases by 35%. How many goats does the farmer now have?

9   Amount A   Amount B

  | Reduce £2800 by 45% | | Increase £1300 by 20% |

  Which amount above is the larger and by how much?

10 Bianca has £640 in her bank account. She decides to use 85% of this money for a holiday.

How much money is left in her bank account?

11

SALE

shirt
£32
25% off

dress
£45
40% off

skirt
£30
20% off

Naomi has £25. Which items above could she buy?

12 Mrs Oliver invests £5400 in a savings scheme. After 3 years her money has increased by 15%. How much money does she now have in the savings scheme?

| **HWK 4M** | **Main Book page 84** |

You may use a calculator.

1 A United Nations army unit is to be made up from soldiers from four nations, as shown in the table.

a Write down how many soldiers are chosen from each country.

b From which country do most of the soldiers come from?

Country	Size of available force	Percentage chosen
UK	1600	3%
Germany	400	7%
Spain	250	12%
New Zealand	1400	2%

2 John buys a house for £294 000. He has to pay a 2.5% tax called stamp duty. How much tax does he pay?

3 Remember: £15.1674 = £15.17 to the nearest penny. Write each amount below to the nearest penny.

a £23.2816 **b** £49.316 **c** £2.0774 **d** £138.5146

4 Work out, giving each answer correct to the nearest penny.

a 26% of £5.19 **b** 31% of £16.46 **c** 8.5% of £29.12 **d** 3.4% of £19.74

5 Joe has £42 and spends 63% of his money. Beth has £73 and spends 78% of her money. Who has more money left and by how much?

6 Terry is building a garage and has used 350 bricks so far. He needs to use a further 82% of the bricks used so far. How many bricks will he use in total?

7

Hannah buys all 3 items above in the sale.
How much does she pay in total?

8 Molly's gas bill is £114 plus an extra 5% VAT (known as value added tax). How much does Molly have to pay in total?

9 Lucy's garage bill is £210 plus an extra 17.5% VAT. How much does Lucy have to pay in total?

10

Last year
Cornet £1.80
Sales 1060

This year
Cornet price increased by 20%
Sales decrease by 20%

Each year Alfonso sells ice-creams at the Banwell festival.

a Did Alfonso make more money, the same money or less money from selling cornets this year compared with last year?

b Write down the difference in the amount of money he made.

2.2 Rounding off and estimating

HWK 1M   **Main Book page 89**

1 Round off these numbers to one decimal place.
  a 8.69   **b** 6.46   **c** 7.132   **d** 4.073
  e 5.243   **f** 10.817   **g** 0.094   **h** 3.044

2 Which of the numbers below round off to 6.78 correct to two decimal places?

6.714   6.769   6.773   6.782   6.774   6.786

3 Work out these on a calculator and then round off the answers correct to two decimal places.

a $\dfrac{6.99}{2.01}$ b $\dfrac{3.8^2}{4.3}$ c $\dfrac{8.21}{\sqrt{53}}$ d $\dfrac{5.14 \times 3.6}{0.93}$

e $\dfrac{5.2}{1.9} + 8.714$ f $\dfrac{5.25}{(1.18 + 3.27)}$ g $\dfrac{5.06^2}{4.27}$ h $\dfrac{3.134}{2.6^2}$

4 Which of the numbers below is the smallest that will round off to 8.14 correct to two decimal places?

8.138   8.135   8.141   8.1354   8.1357   8.132

5 How many numbers below round off to 4.8 correct to one decimal place?

4.861   4.841   4.793   4.852   4.768   4.739

6 Reuben rounds off 6.01045 to three decimal places. He writes the answer 6.011. Is this correct? Give a reason for your answer.

7 What is the smallest number which rounds off to 9.3 correct to one decimal place?

8 What is the smallest number which rounds off to 2.38 correct to two decimal places?

HWK 2M ──────────────────────────────── **Main Book page 91**

1 Write the following numbers to two significant figures.

a 7.6145   b 16.285   c 0.08267   d 38 210

e 0.60712   f 0.008749   g 2143   h 387.64

2 Work out $\dfrac{3.8 + 6.14}{0.09^2}$, giving the answer to three significant figures.

3 Work out the area of this triangle, giving the answer to three significant figures.

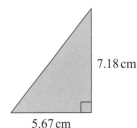

7.18 cm

5.67 cm

4 6641.08 is 7000 when rounded to one significant figure. True or false?
If false, what is the true answer?

5 What is the smallest number which rounds off to 4.87 correct to three significant figures?

6 Work out these questions on a calculator and then round off the answers to three significant figures.

a $\dfrac{5.16 + 9.3}{3.7}$ 　　b $\dfrac{46}{9} + 3.89$ 　　c $\dfrac{7.63}{8.2^2} + \dfrac{5.17}{1.3^2}$ 　　d $\dfrac{5.68^2 - 17.4}{\sqrt{32.9}}$

7 Write the following numbers to the amount of significant figures (s.f.) indicated.

a 0.871 (1 s.f.) 　　　　b 3278 (3 s.f.) 　　　　c 0.08071 (2 s.f.)

d 783.62 (2 s.f.) 　　　　e 0.041082 (4 s.f.) 　　　f 63.0218 (3 s.f.)

g 5.70318 (3 s.f.) 　　　h 81905 (2 s.f.) 　　　　i 0.00382 (1 s.f.)

8 Jamilla says that 0.080463 is equal to 0.080 when rounded to two significant figures.
Is she correct or not? Give a reason for your answer.

HWK 3M ——————————————————————— **Main Book page 92**

1 Work out 40×20

2 Work out a rough estimate for 39×22

3 Work out 8×700

4 Work out a rough estimate for 7.93×706

5 Work out a rough estimate for 51×8.98

6 Do not use a calculator. Decide, by estimating, which of the three answers is closest to the exact answer.

	Calculation	A	B	C
a	7.3 × 31	2100	210	100
b	14.9 × 9.98	150	25	1500
c	24.8 × 40.2	100	1000	200
d	19.6 × 4.94	500	100	10
e	6.01 × 29.8	180	18	360
f	59.7 × 71.1	420	840	4200
g	403 ÷ 79.12	32 000	50	5
h	899 ÷ 1.98	450	1800	45
i	51 ÷ 0.99	50	5	200
j	607 ÷ 21.8	3	120	30
k	79.3 + 81 + 139	300	200	400
l	9.6 × 90.4	450	900	90
m	231 + 19.6 + 41.3	200	390	290
n	19.7 × 31.06	60	300	600
o	196 ÷ 51.3	4	80	40

HWK 4M ———————————————————— **Main Book page 93**

Do not use a calculator for these questions.

1 Gareth needs to buy 19 packets of cereal at £2.49 for each packet. Estimate the total cost.

2 A book weighs 292 g. Estimate how much 31 books would weigh.

3 A book costs £9.95. Estimate the cost of 152 books.

4 Write down each calculation below and match it to the correct answer from the list given.

a 20.6 ÷ 5   b 49 × 20.2   c 8.1 × 32   d 42 × 6.8

e 2.8 + 13.9   f 3012 ÷ 4.8

Answers:	259.2	16.7	989.8	627.5	4.12	285.6

5 Caitlin covers 0.79 m every time she takes a stride. Estimate the distance she travels if she takes 994 strides.

6 Ryan sells cups of tea for 82p each from his stall. One weekend he sells 396 cups of tea. It costs him £130 to make the tea and sort out the cups. Estimate the profit he makes on selling cups of tea during this weekend.

7 Write down each calculation below and match it to the correct answer from the list given.

a $31.8 \div 4$ **b** 79×9.8 **c** $\sqrt{37.5769}$

d 10.3×4.1 **e** 29% of 1380   **f** $348.89 \div 5.02$

| Answers: | 42.23 | 6.13 | 7.95 | 69.5 | 774.2 | 400.2 |

8

box of paper	£4.95
ink cartridge	£13.10
pack of photo paper	£7.99

Louisa buys three boxes of paper, two ink cartridges and one pack of photo paper. Roughly how much change would Louisa get from £50?

2.3 Drawing graphs

HWK 1M   **Main Book page 98**

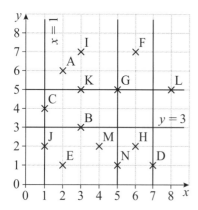

Look at the grid opposite.

1 Write down the coordinates of points M and F.

2 Letter B lies on the line $y = 3$. Which line does the letter K lie on?

3 Which letters lie on the line $x = 1$?

4 Which letters lie on $x = 7$?

5 Which letters lie on $x = 5$?

6 Which letter lies on $y = 6$?

7 Which letter lies on $x = 4$?

8 Letter G lies on $x = 5$ and $y = 5$.
What letter lies on $x = 2$ and $y = 6$?

9 What letter lies on $x = 6$ and $y = 7$?

10 What letter lies on $x = 1$ and $y = 2$?

11 Write down the equation of the line which passes through G and L.

12 Write down the equation of the line which passes through E, N and D.

Look at the grid opposite.

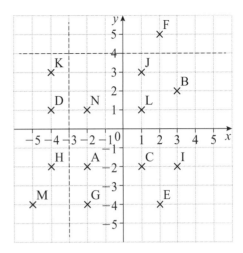

13 Write down the coordinates of points C and K.

14 Letter J lies on the line $x = 1$. Which other letters lie on this line?

15 Letter E lies on the line $y = -4$. Which other letters lie on this line?

16 Which letters lie on the line $y = 1$?

17 Which letters lie on the line $x = -4$?

18 Write down the equation of the line which passes through the letters B and I.

19 Write down the equation of the line which passes through the letters K and J.

20 Write down the equation of the horizontal broken line.

21 What letter lies on $x = -4$ and $y = -2$?

22 What letter lies on $x = -2$ and $y = 1$?

23 Write down the equation of the vertical broken line.

24 Write down the equation of the horizontal line which passes through four of the letters shown.

25 Write down the equations of the two lines which meet at point F.

26 Write down the equations of the two lines which meet at point A.

HWK 2M ──────────────────────── **Main Book page 100**

For each question, copy and complete the table, then draw the graph using the scales given.

1 $y = 2x + 2$ for x-values from 0 to 5

$2x + 2$ means $\boxed{x} \longrightarrow \boxed{\times 2} \longrightarrow \boxed{+2}$

x	0	1	2	3	4	5
y					10	
coordinates					(4, 10)	

(x-axis: use 1 cm for 1 unit
y-axis: use 1 cm for 2 units)

2 $y = 5 - x$ for x-values from 0 to 5

$5 - x$ means $\boxed{5} \longrightarrow \boxed{-x}$

x	0	1	2	3	4	5
y			3			
coordinates			(2, 3)			

(x-axis: use 1 cm for 1 unit
y-axis: use 1 cm for 1 unit)

3 $y = 3x + 1$ for x-values from 0 to 5

$3x + 1$ means $\boxed{x} \longrightarrow \boxed{\times 3} \longrightarrow \boxed{+1}$

(x-axis: 1 cm for 1 unit, y-axis: 1 cm for 2 units)

4 $y = \dfrac{1}{2}x + 2$ for x-values from 0 to 6

$\dfrac{1}{2}x + 2$ means $\boxed{x} \longrightarrow \boxed{\times \frac{1}{2}} \longrightarrow \boxed{+2}$

(x-axis: 1 cm for 1 unit, y-axis: 2 cm for 1 unit)

5 $y = 10 - 2x$ for x-values from 0 to 5 (x-axis: 1 cm for 1 unit, y-axis: 1 cm for 1 unit)

HWK 2E ———————————————————————————— **Main Book page 102**

Draw the graph for each equation in questions **1** to **5**.

1 $y = x^2 + 4$ for x-values from -3 to 3

2 $y = x^2 - 2$ for x-values from -3 to 3

3 $y = (x - 1)^2$ for x-values from -2 to 4

4 $y = x^2 + 2x$ for x-values from -3 to 3

5 $y = x^2 - 6x + 9$ for x-values from 0 to 6

1   The temperature in a house was recorded every two hours for a whole day; the results are shown below.

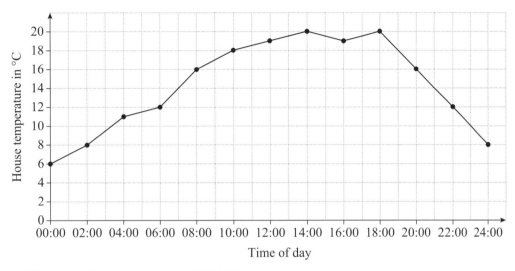

a   What was the temperature at 10.00 h?

b   What was the temperature at 20.00 h?

c   What was the temperature at 02.00 h?

d   At which two times was the temperature 16°C?

e   At which two times was the temperature 20°C?

f   What was the temperature at 23.00 h?

2   One gallon is approximately 4.5 litres.

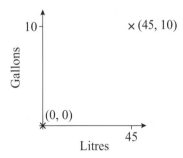

a   Draw axes, as shown, with a scale of 1 cm for 1 gallon and 1 cm for 5 litres. Draw a '×' where 45 litres are equal to 10 gallons. Draw another '×' at (0, 0).

b   Draw a long straight line through the two points above and use your graph to convert

    i   2 gallons into litres

    ii   37.5 litres into gallons.

c   Ben puts 13.5 litres of petrol into his car. This costs him £15.45. Use your graph to help you calculate the cost of 1 gallon of petrol.

3 A man climbing a mountain measures his height above sea level after every 30 minutes; the results are shown below.

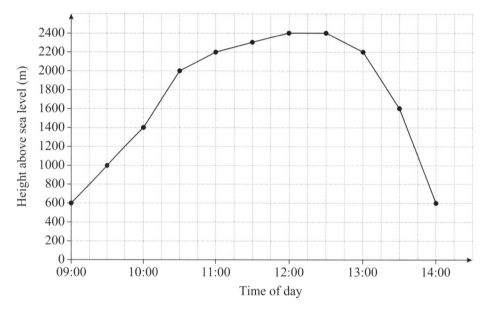

a At what height was he at 10:00 h?

b At what height was he at 13:30 h?

c Estimate his height above sea level at 09:45 h.

d Estimate his altitude at 10:45 h.

e Estimate his height above sea level at 13:45 h.

f At what two times was he 2200 m above sea level?

g How high was the mountain? (He got to the top!)

h How long did he rest at the summit?

i How long did he take to reach the summit?

HWK 4M   **Main Book page 104**

1 Using the same axes, draw the graphs of

$$y = 3x - 1, \ y = 3x - 3, \ y = 3x \text{ and } y = 3x + 3$$

Write down what you notice about each line and its equation.

(Clues: where do the lines cut the y-axis? – are the lines parallel?)

2 Three of the lines below are parallel. Write down the equation of the line which is *not* parallel to the other lines.

| $y = 4x + 1$ | $y = 3x + 4$ | $y = 4x - 2$ | $y = 4x + 4$ |

3 Which line below does not cross the y-axis at $(0, 5)$?

| $y = 5x - 1$ | $y = 2x + 5$ | $y = 5x + 5$ |

In questions **1** to **10** you are given the coordinates of several points on a line.

Find the equation of each line.

1

x	1	2	3	4	5
y	5	6	7	8	9

2

x	1	2	3	4	5
y	10	11	12	13	14

3

x	9	8	7	6	5
y	5	4	3	2	1

4

x	5	6	7	8	9
y	4	3	2	1	0

5

x	1	2	3	4	5
y	5	10	15	20	25

6

x	4	5	6	7	8	9
y	19	20	21	22	23	24

7

x	10	12	14	16	18
y	4	6	8	10	12

8

x	20	19	18	17	16
y	0	1	2	3	4

9

x	2	4	6	8	10
y	16	32	48	64	80

10

x	1	2	3	4	5
y	1	3	5	7	9

11

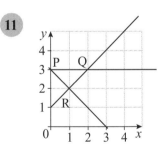

Find the equation of the line through

a R and Q

b P and Q

c P and R

2.4 Sequences 1

1   Write down the rule for each sequence.

   a 3.3, 3.1, 2.9, 2.7, …   **b** 3.5, 7, 14, 28, …

   c 60, 6, 0.6, 0.06, …   **d** −7, −5, −3, −1, …

2 Write down each sequence and find the missing numbers.

a | 3 | 12 | 48 | ☐ | ☐ |

b | −4 | −1 | ☐ | 5 | 8 | ☐ |

c | ☐ | ☐ | ☐ | 11 | 6 | 1 |

3 **a**

Draw the next row which will fit onto the bottom of this triangle.

b How many circles are used in total for the triangle in part **a** if seven rows are drawn?

4 Luke says the next number in the sequence ☐1☐ ☐2☐ ☐4☐ is ☐8☐. Ali says that Luke is wrong and the next number is ☐7☐. Tom says that Luke and Ali are both correct. *Explain* why.

5 The first term of a sequence is 4. Write down the first four terms of the sequence if the rule is

a double and subtract 1   **b** multiply by 3 and add 1   **c** double and add 4

6 Find the missing numbers in these linear sequences.

a | 6 | ☐ | 14 | 18 | ☐ | ☐ |

b | ☐ | 23 | 16 | ☐ | 2 | ☐ |

c | ☐ | 49 | ☐ | ☐ | ☐ | 17 |

7 An arithmetic sequence has a 3rd term of 15 and a 4th term of 19.
What is the 2nd term?

8 An arithmetic sequence has a 1st term of 7 and a 3rd term of 19.
What is the 4th term?

9 The rule for this sequence is 'multiply by 2 and add 2'. Find the missing numbers.

10 Write down the rule for this sequence.

1 Here is a sequence: 5, 7, 10, 14 …
Write the numbers in a table
as shown.

Predict the numbers shown with (?)
to find the next two terms in the
sequence 5, 7, 10, 14, …

Terms	Differences
5	
	2
7	
	3
10	
	4
14	
	(?)
(?)	
	(?)
(?)	

2 Below are three sequences. Use differences to predict the next two numbers in each sequence.

a | 3 | 8 | 15 | 24 | ? | ? |

b | 53 | 41 | 31 | 23 | ? | ? |

c | 80 | 71 | 63 | 56 | ? | ? |

3 Here is a sequence of matchstick squares.

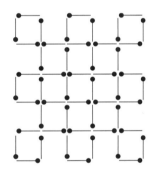

$n = 1$ $n = 2$ $n = 3$

Shape number, n	Number of matches	Difference
1	4	
		16
2	20	
		32
3	52	
		48
4	100	
5	?	

Use the differences to predict the number of matches in shape number 5

4 Predict the next two terms in each sequence.
a 24, 39, 57, 78, …   **b** 7, 19, 35, 55, …   **c** 2, 16, 39, 71, …

2.5 Reflection and enlargement

1   Copy each shape onto squared paper and draw the image after reflection in the broken line.

a 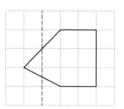   **b** 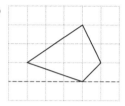   **c**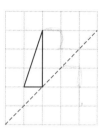

d 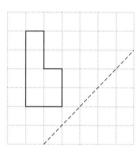   **e** 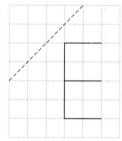   **f**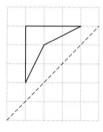

In questions **2** to **4** , copy each shape and draw the image after reflection in the broken line.

2 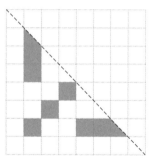   **3** 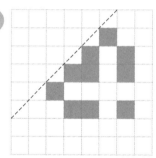   **4**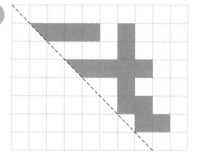

5   First reflect the shape in line 1 and then reflect the image in line 2.

a 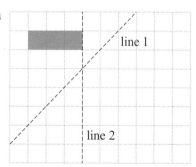   **b**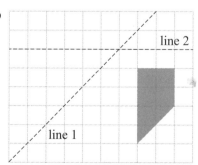

1 Copy the diagram onto squared paper.

  a Reflect triangle P in $y = x$.
     Label the image Q.

  b Reflect triangle Q in $x = 2$.
     Label the image R.

  c Reflect triangle R in the x-axis.
     Label the image S.

  d Write down the coordinates
     of the vertices of triangle S.

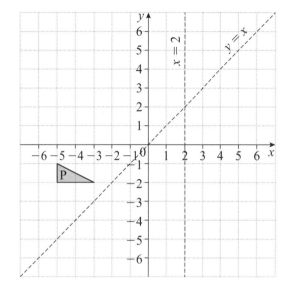

2 **a** Draw x and y axes with values from -5 to 5 and draw shape A which has vertices
     (corners) at (2, 2), (2, 3), (5, 3) and (5, 2).

  b Reflect shape A in the x-axis. Label the image B.

  c Reflect shape B in $x = 1$. Label the image C.

  d Reflect shape C in $y = 1$. Label the image D.

  e Write down the coordinates of the vertices of shape D.

3

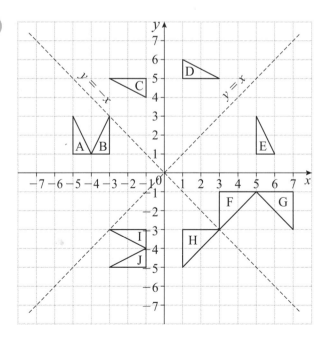

Write down the equation of
the mirror line for each of the
following reflections.

  a A → B

  b B → E

  c I → J

  d D → E

  e A → C

  f C → J

  g H → F

  h F → G

1 Enlarge this shape
by scale factor 3

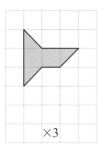

×3

In questions **2** to **5** , look at each pair of diagrams and decide whether or not one diagram is an enlargement of the other. For each question, write the scale factor of the enlargement or write 'not an enlargement'.

2

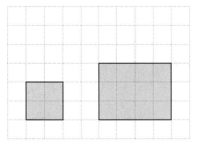

3

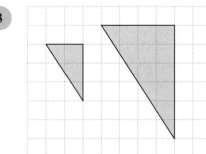

4

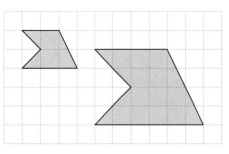

5

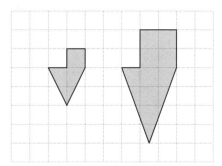

6 3 cm | A | 8 cm

B 12 cm 4.5 cm

Is rectangle A an enlargement of rectangle B?
Explain your answer.

7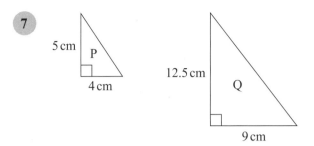

Is triangle Q an enlargement of triangle P? *Explain* your answer.

8 Draw an enlargement of this picture with scale factor 2. Shade in the letters with different colours.

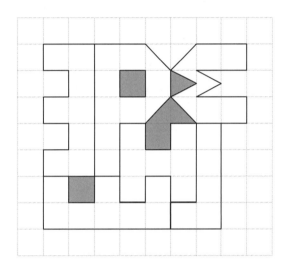

9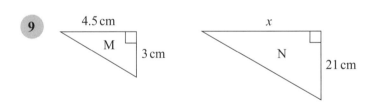

Triangle N is an enlargement of triangle M. Calculate the value of x.

10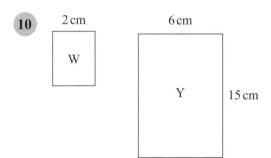

Rectangle Y is an enlargement of rectangle W. Calculate the area of rectangle W.

In questions **1** to **6** , copy the diagram and then draw an enlargement using the scale factor and centre of enlargement given. Leave room for the enlargement.

1
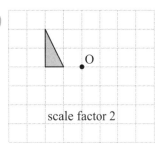
scale factor 2

2
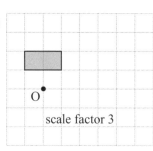
scale factor 3

3
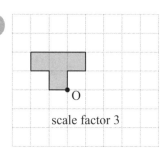
scale factor 3

4
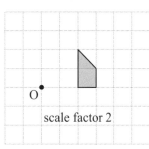
scale factor 2

5
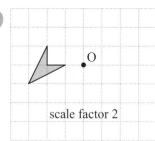
scale factor 2

6
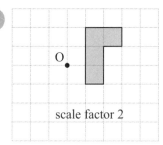
scale factor 2

7

a Copy this diagram.

b Enlarge shape A with scale factor 2 and centre of enlargement (0, 0).

c Enlarge shape B with scale factor 4 and centre of enlargement (0, 0).

d Enlarge shape C with scale factor 3 and centre of enlargement (0, 0).

e Enlarge shape D with scale factor 2 and centre of enlargement (0, 0).

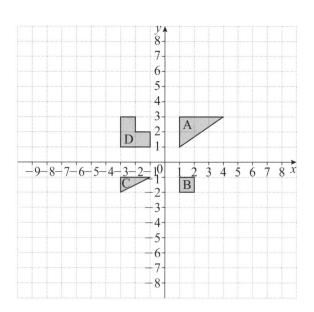

HWK 5M ─────────────────────────── **Main Book page 128**

Draw the shapes and then draw lines through corresponding points to find the centre of enlargement.
Do not draw the shapes too near the edge of the page!

1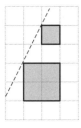

2

3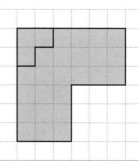

4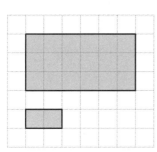

5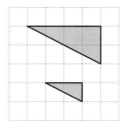

6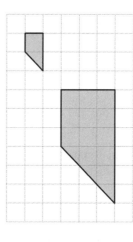

7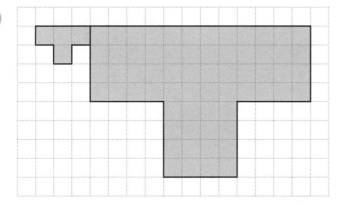

8 Shape P is enlarged about (0, 0) by scale factor $\frac{1}{3}$ to give shape Q.

Shape Q is enlarged about (0, 0) by scale factor $\frac{1}{2}$ to give shape R.

If shape R is enlarged about (0, 0) to give the original shape P, what scale factor is used?

2.6 Rotation and combined transformations

In questions **1** to **3**, draw the shape and then draw and shade its new position (the image) when it is rotated by the angle shown. Take O as the centre of rotation in each case.

1
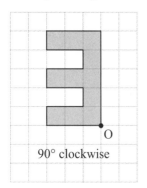
90° clockwise

2
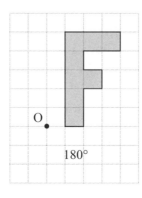
180°

3
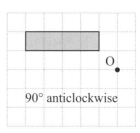
90° anticlockwise

4 Copy the diagram shown, using axes from −6 to 6

  a Rotate shape P 90° anticlockwise about (0, 0). Label the new shape R.

  b Rotate triangle Q 90° clockwise about (4, −1). Label the new shape S.

  c Rotate shape Q 180° about (0, 0). Label the new shape T.

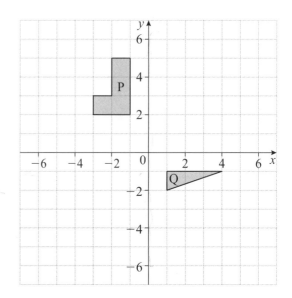

5 **a** Draw axes with values from −6 to 6 and draw triangle P with vertices at (−3, −2), (−3, −6) and (−5, −2).

  b Rotate triangle P 90° anticlockwise about (0, 0). Draw and label the new triangle Q.

  c Rotate triangle Q 90° anticlockwise about (2, −2). Draw and label the new triangle R.

  d Rotate triangle R 180° about (3, 2). Draw and label the new triangle S.

  e Rotate triangle S 90° anticlockwise about (0, 0). Draw and label the new triangle T. Write down the coordinates of each vertex (corner) of triangle T.

In questions **1** and **2**, copy each diagram. Use tracing paper to find the centre of each rotation.

1

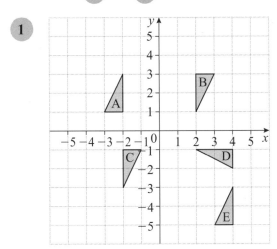

a rotation of △A onto △B

b rotation of △A onto △C

c rotation of △B onto △D

d rotation of △C onto △E

2   **a** rotation of shape P onto shape Q

b rotation of shape Q onto shape R

c rotation of shape Q onto shape S

d rotation of shape S onto shape T

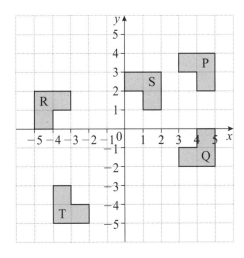

50

1 Copy this diagram.

a Translate triangle A by $\begin{pmatrix} -6 \\ -1 \end{pmatrix}$

and label the new triangle B.

b Rotate triangle B 180° about $(-3, 0)$.
Label the new triangle C.

c Reflect triangle C in the y-axis.
Label the new triangle D.

d Translate triangle D by $\begin{pmatrix} 0 \\ -1 \end{pmatrix}$

and label the new triangle E.

e What single transformation will move
triangle E onto triangle A?

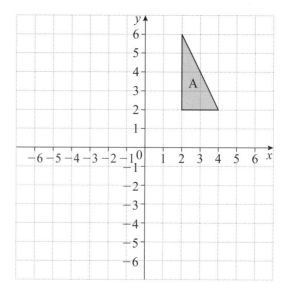

2 Copy this diagram.

a Rotate shape P 90° anticlockwise about $(0, 0)$.
Label the new shape Q.

b Reflect shape Q in the y-axis. Label the new
shape R.

c Rotate shape R 90° anticlockwise about $(1, -2)$.
Label the new shape S.

d Reflect shape S in the y-axis. Label the new
shape T.

e Describe the single transformation which
will move shape T onto shape P (i.e. write
down the translation vector).

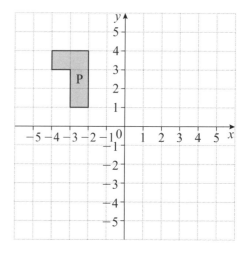

51

3

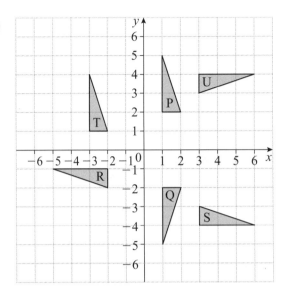

Describe fully the following transformations.

a triangle P onto triangle Q

b triangle Q onto triangle R

c triangle Q onto triangle S

d triangle P onto triangle T

e triangle P onto triangle U

f triangle S onto triangle U

UNIT 3

3.1 Area and perimeter

HWK 1M ———————————————————————————— **Main Book page 160**

1   Calculate the area of each shape. The lengths are in cm.

a

b

c

d

e

f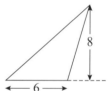

2   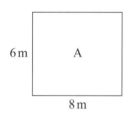

a Find the area of shape A.

b Find the area of shape B.

c Find the total area of both shape A and shape B.

d Find the area of this shape.

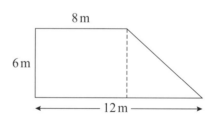

3   Calculate the area of each shape. The lengths are in cm.

a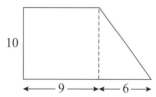

b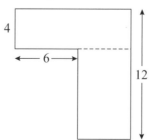

c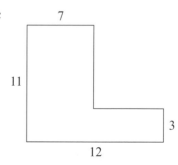

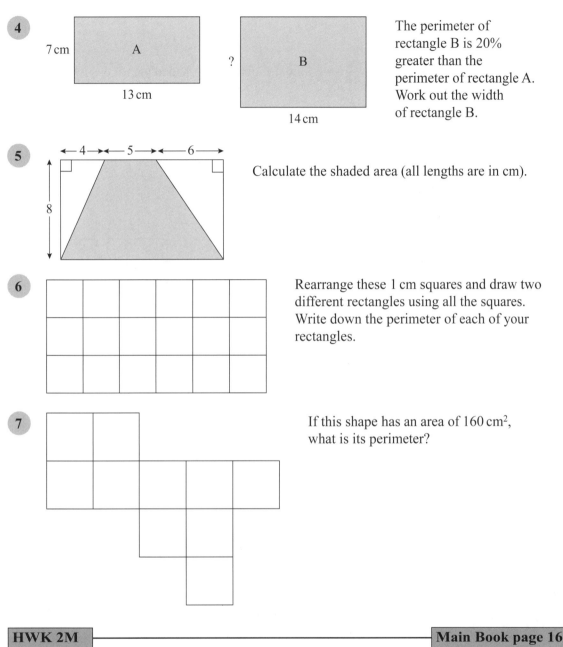

4 A: 7 cm, 13 cm

? B 14 cm

The perimeter of rectangle B is 20% greater than the perimeter of rectangle A. Work out the width of rectangle B.

5 ← 4 → ← 5 → ← 6 → 8

Calculate the shaded area (all lengths are in cm).

6 Rearrange these 1 cm squares and draw two different rectangles using all the squares. Write down the perimeter of each of your rectangles.

7 If this shape has an area of 160 cm², what is its perimeter?

HWK 2M ————————————————— **Main Book page 162**

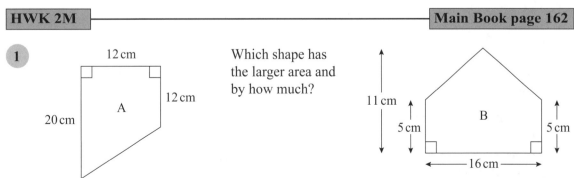

1 12 cm

A 20 cm, 12 cm

Which shape has the larger area and by how much?

11 cm

5 cm B 5 cm

← 16 cm →

2 Work out the perimeter of a regular pentagon of side 7 cm

3 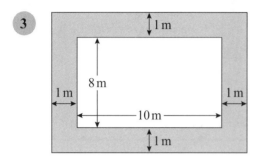 Find the area of this shaded path.

4 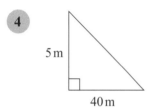 These two shapes have the same area. Find the length of the side marked x.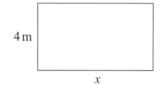

5 Alice wishes to carpet this room.

  a What is the area of the room?

  b The carpet costs £15.85 per square metre. How much will Alice pay for the carpet?

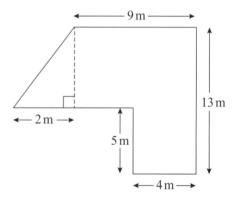

6 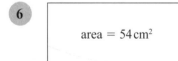 The length of this rectangle is 3 cm greater than its width. Find the perimeter of this rectangle.

7 Jed is putting tiles onto a rectangular wall which measures 3 m by 5 m. Each tile is a square with side 10 cm. A box of 25 tiles costs £9.85

  a How many tiles does Jed need?

  b How much will Jed have to pay for the tiles?

  c Jed ends up breaking 5% of the tiles. How much *extra* must he spend on the tiles to finish the job?

8

square A

Square A has a perimeter of 24 cm. Rectangle B has the same area as square A. Calculate the value of x shown on the diagram.

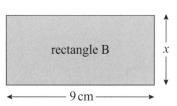

rectangle B

x

← 9 cm →

HWK 3M **Main Book page 164**

Remember: area of parallelogram = base × height

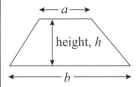

a

height, h

b

area of trapezium = $\frac{1}{2}h(a + b)$

1 Calculate the area of each shape. The lengths are in cm.

a

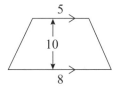

5

10

8

b

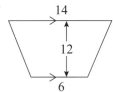

14

12

6

c

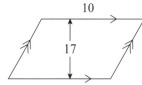

10

17

d

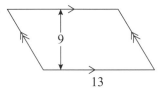

9

13

e

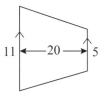

11 ← 20 → 5

f

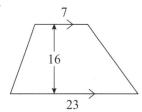

7

16

23

2 Calculate the value of x in each parallelogram below.

a

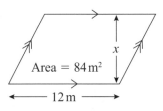

x

Area = 84 m²

← 12 m →

b

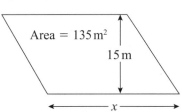

Area = 135 m²

15 m

x

56

3

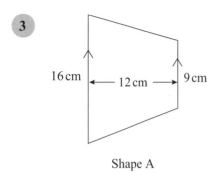

Shape A

Which shape has
the larger area and
by how much?

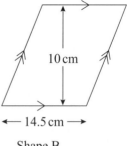

Shape B

4 Find the area of this shape.

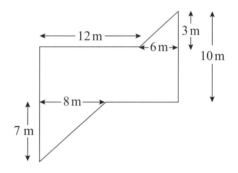

5 Imagine the area of the trapezium
shown is 60 cm². Write down
possible values for *a* and *b*.

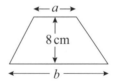

6 Ashley has to paint one side of his house.
Each pot of paint covers 20 m².
How many pots of paint will Ashley
need to buy to do the job?

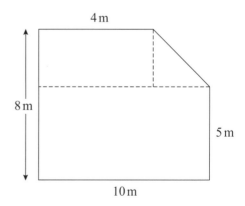

3.2 Circles

For each of the circles shown below, write down

a the radius   **b** the diameter (you must give the units).

1   **2**   **3**   **4**   **5**

6   **7**   **8**   **9**   **10**

> Remember: circumference = $\pi \times$ diameter

Give all answers to one decimal place.

1   Calculate the circumference of each circle.

a   **b**   **c**   **d**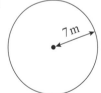

2   A circular pond has a diameter of 30 m. Calculate its circumference.

3   A coin has a radius of 8 mm. Find its circumference.

4      Tom walks once around the edge of a 60 m length square field.
Anna walks once around the edge of an 80 m diameter circular field.
Who walks further and by how much?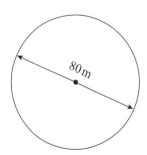

60 m

5

In a game show, a comedian lies on a circular turntable.
The comedian is 1.7 m tall.
If the turntable is spun around four complete rotations,
how far does the top of the comedian's head travel?

6 All the lines shown
opposite are white
lines on a sports field.
Work out the total
length of the white
lines that all need
to be painted over
by the groundsperson.

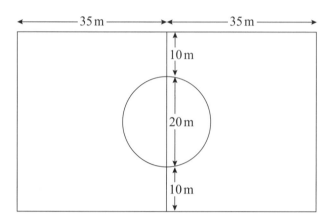

HWK 3M **Main Book page 171**

Calculate the perimeter of each shape. All shapes are either semicircles or quarter circles.
Give answers correct to one decimal place.

1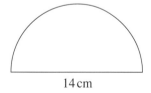

14 cm

2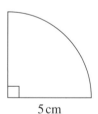

5 cm

3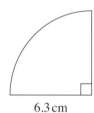

6.3 cm

4

A 18 cm

Which shape has the longer perimeter
and by how much?

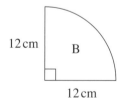

12 cm B

12 cm

5

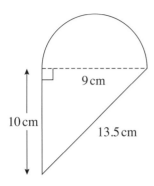

9 cm

10 cm

13.5 cm

This shape is made from a triangle and a semicircle. Calculate the total perimeter of this shape.

6 Cameron runs twice around track A. Eloise runs twice around track B. How much further does Cameron run than Eloise?

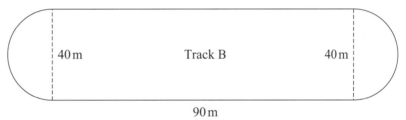

50 m   Track A   50 m

← 80 m →

40 m   Track B   40 m

90 m

| **HWK 4M** | **Main Book page 173** |

Remember: area of a circle = πr^2

Give answers correct to one decimal place.

1 Find the area of a circular road sign with diameter 42 cm

2 Find the area of a circular plate which has a radius of 11 cm

3

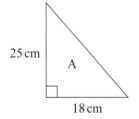

25 cm

A

18 cm

Which shape has the larger area and by how much?

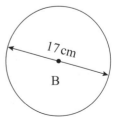

17 cm

B

60

4 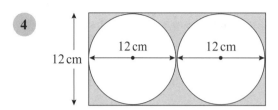 Calculate the shaded area.

5 Work out the area of each shape.

a 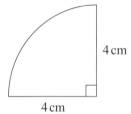   **b** 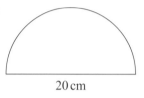   **c**

6 A circular lawn has a diameter of 60 m. In the centre of the lawn is a circular pond with a radius of 5 m. What is the area of the lawn without the pond?

7 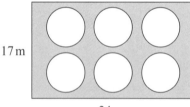 The shaded part of this design is to be painted blue.
Each circle has a diameter of 7 m.
Calculate the area to be painted blue.

8 This shape is made from a rectangle and a quarter circle. Calculate the total area of the shape.

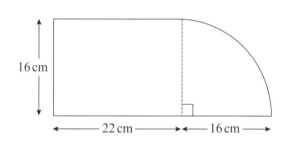

3.3 Number – calculations review

HWK 1M   **Main Book page 178**

Work out, without a calculator.

1 $68 \div 10$	**2** 9.3×100	**3** 0.169×1000	**4** $0.25 - 0.142$
5 $94 \div 100$	**6** $13.6 + 27$	**7** $1.04 \div 4$	**8** $0.392 \div 7$
9 5.8×1000	**10** $0.82 - 0.073$	**11** $36 + 16.2$	**12** $46 \div 1000$

13
packet of crisps 48p
bottle of water £1.06
currant bun 39p

Sally buys 3 packets of crisps, 2 bottles of water and 2 currant buns. How much change will she get from £10?

14 How many currant buns in question **13** could you buy with £5?

15 Which is larger and by how much?

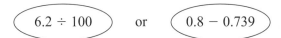

6.2 ÷ 100   or   0.8 − 0.739

16 One hundred 'Calypso' chocolates cost £23.60. One thousand 'Midnight' chocolates cost £235. Which chocolate is the most expensive and by how much per chocolate?

17 What is 0.01 less than 2.3?

18 Which calculation gives a different answer to the other two?

16.5 + 9.38   31.4 − 8.18   33 − 7.12

19 Write the number that is half way between 4.1 and 4.2

20 Write the number that is half way between 3.67 and 3.68

21 Write down the largest number shown below.

8.6   8.62   8.602   8.594   8.59   8.567   8.7

22 Write down the second largest number from the list of numbers in question **21**.

23 Colin weighs 63.64 kg and Marie weighs 51.87 kg. How much heavier is Colin?

24 Charlie is sponsored 20p per kilometre for a charity run. How much money is he given if he runs 13.8 km?

62

Copy and complete this crossnumber *without using a calculator*.

1			2		3		4

Across

1	427 × 6
3	9350 ÷ 10
5	68 × 6
6	42 × 200
8	30 × 25
9	396 ÷ 6
10	672 ÷ 8
12	517 − 432
13	2422 ÷ 7
15	840 ÷ 12
16	928 ÷ 32
17	688 ÷ 43
18	5924 + 2450
19	161 × 5

Down

1	3081 − 895
2	56 × 43
3	1155 − 168
4	18 × 300
7	2924 + 1756
11	6881 − 2485
14	231 × 30
15	1117 − 389
16	1284 ÷ 6

For each of the scales, work out the measurement shown by each arrow.

1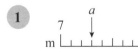

2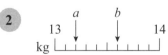

3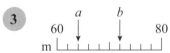

4

5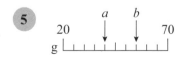

6

7 Work out the difference between *b* and *a* for each scale shown below.

a kg

6

←—*b*

←—*a*

2

b litres

5

←—*b*

←—*a*

1

c metres

10

←—*b*

←—*a*

6

8 Copy the line and locate the numbers.

| 4.02 | 3.96 | 3.92 | 4.08 | 4.06 |

3.9   4.1

|,,,,,,,,,,,|,,,,,,,,,,,|

HWK 4M ————————————————————————— **Main Book page 181**

1 Copy and fill in each empty box.

a $\dfrac{4}{5} = \dfrac{\square}{20}$ **b** $\dfrac{3}{7} = \dfrac{\square}{35}$ **c** $\dfrac{5}{9} = \dfrac{30}{\square}$ **d** $\dfrac{7}{8} = \dfrac{42}{\square}$

2 Which fraction below is not equivalent to the others?

$$\dfrac{12}{18} \quad \dfrac{18}{27} \quad \dfrac{4}{6} \quad \dfrac{16}{24} \quad \dfrac{10}{15} \quad \dfrac{21}{28} \quad \dfrac{20}{30}$$

3 Work out the following, cancelling where possible.

a $\dfrac{2}{5} + \dfrac{1}{3}$ **b** $\dfrac{7}{8} - \dfrac{2}{3}$ **c** $\dfrac{5}{6} - \dfrac{3}{4}$ **d** $\dfrac{9}{10} - \dfrac{3}{5}$

e $\dfrac{1}{4} + \dfrac{3}{5}$ **f** $\dfrac{3}{7} + \dfrac{2}{9}$ **g** $\dfrac{7}{10} - \dfrac{1}{3}$ **h** $\dfrac{7}{8} - \dfrac{2}{5}$

4 Each week Kelly spends $\frac{1}{3}$ of her money on rent and $\frac{2}{5}$ of her money on food. What total fraction of her money does she spend on her rent and food?

5 $\frac{4}{7}$ of a garden is covered by a lawn and $\frac{1}{3}$ is paved. What fraction of the garden is *not* a lawn and *not* paved?

64

6 Work out, leaving each answer as a mixed number.

a $1\frac{1}{3} + \frac{1}{4}$ b $2\frac{1}{2} - \frac{3}{5}$ c $3\frac{1}{4} - 1\frac{1}{3}$

d $2\frac{1}{4} + 1\frac{1}{10}$ e $1\frac{2}{3} + 3\frac{1}{2}$ f $3\frac{1}{3} - 2\frac{1}{2}$

7

The fractions show what proportion of this jigsaw each piece covers. What fraction of the jigsaw is covered by the shaded piece?

HWK 5M ———————————————————— **Main Book page 182**

1 Janet has £96. She spends $\frac{5}{8}$ of her money on a jacket. How much money does she have left?

2 Work out

a $\frac{5}{9}$ of 72   b $\frac{3}{7}$ of 42   c $\frac{7}{10}$ of 50   d $\frac{2}{5}$ of 60

3 A shop increases all its prices by $\frac{2}{9}$. Write down the new cost of each item shown below.

| trousers £36 | shirt £27 | coat £108 |

4 Toni runs for $\frac{7}{12}$ of 4 hours. How many minutes does she run for?

5 Hans needs to use $\frac{9}{25}$ of his flour to bake. If he has 2 kg of flour to start with, how much flour will he have left after baking?

6 Decrease 72 by $\frac{5}{6}$

7 Work out, cancelling when possible.

a $\frac{5}{6} \times \frac{1}{4}$ b $\frac{3}{7} \times \frac{2}{5}$ c $\frac{5}{8} \times \frac{3}{4}$ d $\frac{4}{9} \times \frac{3}{7}$

e $\frac{3}{8} \times \frac{5}{6}$ f $\frac{2}{7} \times \frac{3}{4}$ g $\frac{6}{7} \times \frac{2}{3}$ h $\frac{3}{5} \times \frac{5}{6}$

i $\frac{4}{9} \times \frac{18}{1}$ j $\frac{5}{6} \times 24$ k $\frac{9}{10} \times 30$ l $\frac{3}{8} \times 4$

8 Work out

a $\dfrac{1}{3} \div \dfrac{5}{8}$ b $\dfrac{2}{7} \div \dfrac{1}{2}$ c $\dfrac{3}{5} \div \dfrac{7}{10}$ d $\dfrac{1}{4} \div \dfrac{2}{3}$

e $\dfrac{1}{6} \div \dfrac{7}{8}$ f $\dfrac{3}{7} \div \dfrac{3}{4}$ g $\dfrac{3}{10} \div \dfrac{5}{9}$ h $\dfrac{2}{5} \div \dfrac{7}{12}$

HWK 6M   **Main Book page 183**

1 Ben is running a $3\frac{1}{2}$ km race. He leads for the first $\frac{4}{7}$ of the race. How many km is this?

2

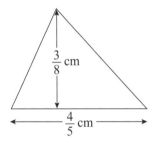

Work out the area of this triangle.

(Remember: area $= \frac{1}{2}$ base $\times$ height)

3 Work out

a $2\dfrac{1}{2} \times \dfrac{3}{5}$ b $1\dfrac{3}{4} \times 3\dfrac{1}{3}$ c $2\dfrac{2}{5} \times 2\dfrac{1}{2}$

4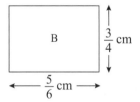

Which rectangle has the larger area and by how much?

5 Work out

a $1\dfrac{1}{2} \div \dfrac{7}{10}$ b $2\dfrac{3}{4} \div 1\dfrac{1}{3}$ c $2\dfrac{2}{5} \div 3\dfrac{2}{3}$

6 Charles has $13\frac{3}{4}$ kg of flour. He puts all this flour into $1\frac{1}{4}$ kg bags.
How many bags does he fill with flour?

HWK 7M   **Main Book page 185**

1 Work out

a 5×0.01 b 32×0.1 c 0.2×0.3 d 0.7×0.4

e 0.3×0.06 f 5×0.6 g 3×0.05 h 0.2×0.06

i 0.6×0.07 j 0.02×0.04 k 0.03×11 l 0.7×0.008

2 Answer 'true' or 'false'.

    a $0.3^2 = 0.9$ **b** $0.1 \times 0.2 = 0.2$ **c** $0.5^2 = 0.25$

3 A 4 m width of carpet costs £8.35 per metre. Calculate the cost of 6.4 m of carpet.

4 Copy and complete the multiplication square.

×	0.3	0.05	7	1.2	0.9
0.6					
0.05					
1.1					
0.8					
4					

5

Which shape has the larger area and by how much?

A — triangle with 0.9 m height and 1.6 m base.

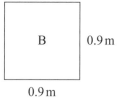

B — square with sides 0.9 m and 0.9 m.

6

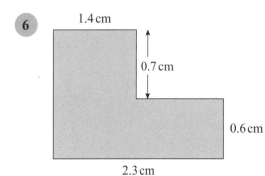

Find the area of this shape.

1.4 cm, 0.7 cm, 0.6 cm, 2.3 cm

HWK 8M   **Main Book page 186**

1 Work out

    a $8 \div 0.1$ **b** $43 \div 0.1$ **c** $0.6 \div 0.1$ **d** $7 \div 0.01$

    e $0.2 \div 0.01$ **f** $22 \div 0.01$ **g** $58 \div 0.1$ **h** $0.9 \div 0.01$

2 How many 0.1 kg amounts of sugar can be obtained from 2.4 kg of sugar?

3 Answer 'true' or 'false'.

a $0.4 \div 0.01 = 4$ b $31 \div 0.1 = 310$ c $45 \div 0.01 = 450$

d $0.8 \div 0.01 = 800$ e $1 \div 0.01 = 100$ f $0.9 \div 0.1 = 9$

4 Find the missing numbers.

a $14 \div \square = 1400$ b $5 \div \square = 50$ c $0.4 \div \square = 40$

d $\square \div 0.1 = 600$ e $3.6 \div \square = 36$ f $8.7 \div \square = 870$

5 How many 0.01 tonne bags of cement can be filled from 2 tonnes of cement?

HWK 8E ──────────────────────────── **Main Book page 187**

1

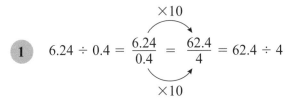

$$6.24 \div 0.4 = \frac{6.24}{0.4} = \frac{62.4}{4} = 62.4 \div 4$$

Work out $4\overline{)62.4}$ to get the final answer.

2 Work out, without a calculator.

a $6.39 \div 0.3$ b $0.72 \div 0.4$ c $0.49 \div 0.2$ d $1.158 \div 0.6$

e $3.78 \div 0.3$ f $0.1174 \div 0.02$ g $0.01352 \div 0.08$ h $9.52 \div 0.7$

i $0.0126 \div 0.09$ j $0.6656 \div 0.8$ k $0.01528 \div 0.002$ l $0.0655 \div 0.005$

3 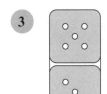 A domino is 4.8 cm long. Hundreds of dominoes are laid in a line 1680 cm long. *Exactly* how many dominoes are used?

4 On average a chocolate raisin weighs 0.9 g. How many chocolate raisins will there be in a packet which weighs 76.5 g?

5 Copy and complete this number chain.

0.07 ──$\times 0.8$──→ [ ] ──$\div 0.02$──→ [ ] ──$\div 0.2$──→ [ ]

6 If $0.7 \times \boxed{?} = 1.12$, find the value of $\boxed{?}$

7 Caroline works at a garage and is paid £8.20 per hour. Scott also works at the garage and is paid £7.50 per hour.

During one week, Caroline earns £164 and Scott earns £240. Work out the total number of hours Caroline and Scott worked during that week.

3.4 Using a calculator

HWK 1M ── **Main Book page 194**

Work out, without a calculator.

1 $16 - 4 \times 2$

2 $20 \div 5 + 3$

3 $9 + 24 \div 6$

4 $41 - 12 \times 3$

5 $8 + 5 \times 2$

6 $(8 + 5) \times 2$

7 $9 \times (15 - 4)$

8 $6 + 6 \times 6$

9 $4 + 2 \times 6 - 3$

10 $(9 - 3) \times (4 + 5)$

11 $17 - 14 \div 2$

12 $5 \times (6 + 2 \times 2)$

13 $36 \div 9 - 22 \div 11$

14 $\dfrac{32}{5 + 3}$

15 $\dfrac{19 - 7}{8 - 2}$

16 Answer 'true' or 'false'.

a $(3 + 4)^2 = 49$

b $8^2 - 4 = 12$

c $8 + 3 \times 2 = 22$

d $5^2 - 3^2 = 16$

e $19 + 3 \times 4 = 31$

f $4 \times (6 + 3) = 27$

g $(4^2 + 2^2) \div 5 = 4$

h $\dfrac{25 - 8 \times 2}{3} = 3$

i $5 + 6^2 \div 9 = 9$

HWK 2M ── **Main Book page 195**

In questions **1** to **9**, find the missing signs $(+, -, \times, \div)$. There are no brackets.

1 8 2 3 = 19

2 5 3 1 = 2

3 4 18 3 = 10

4 20 2 15 = 25

5 9 16 4 = 21

6 5 9 2 = 23

7 16 14 2 1 = 10

8 10 2 3 4 = 17

9 9 4 2 3 = 14

10 Copy each question and insert brackets so that each calculation gives the correct answer.

a $6 + 3 \div 3 = 3$

b $8 - 2 \times 4 = 24$

c $9 + 1 \div 5 = 2$

d $3 \times 6 - 1 = 15$

e $28 \div 2 + 5 = 4$

f $8 + 3 \times 3 = 33$

g $5 + 20 \div 3 + 2 = 5$

h $30 - 20 - 15 = 25$

i $8 - 1 \times 10 - 3 = 49$

j $10 - 6 \div 1 + 3 = 1$

k $13 + 17 \div 5 = 6$

l $15 - 9 + 3 = 3$

Work out with a calculator, giving each answer correct to two decimal places.

1 $\dfrac{61}{4.7} + 3.9$

2 $5.6 - \dfrac{16.4}{13}$

3 $7.49 \times (8.16 - 3.64)$

4 $(1.93 + 4.78) \div 2.38$

5 $\dfrac{12.4 - 5.17}{2.3}$

6 $\dfrac{2.6^2 + 1.35}{4.7}$

7 $5.65 \div (8.2 - 4.16)$

8 $\dfrac{7.92}{1.82 + 3.03}$

9 $\dfrac{(1.78 - 0.114)^2}{0.383}$

10 $\dfrac{1.17}{(0.68 + 0.23)^2}$

11 $\dfrac{9.23 - 2.14}{6.49}$

12 $0.18^2 \times 2.3$

13 $8.36 + 3.7^2$

14 $(3.62 + 2.59)^2$

15 $(7.12 + 4.93 - 1.86)^2 \times 1.6$

16 $\dfrac{5.6}{1.93} + 4.18$

17 $\dfrac{11.6 - 3.14}{2.12 + 5.9}$

18 $0.93^2 + 0.26^2$

19 $(5.1 \times 2.48) + (3.6 \times 2.9)$

20 $\dfrac{7.94}{2.16^2}$

21 $(8.29 - 2.11)^2$

22 $\dfrac{1.93^2}{5.06 - 2.1}$

23 $(7.62^2 \times 4.9) - 1.6^2$

24 $\dfrac{8.62 + 3.59}{21.4 - 6.28}$

25   Jade sells security devices. She makes 8 selling trips to the north-west of England during one month. Each trip costs her £49.50. During the month she sells 7 burglar alarms and 12 security spotlights. She makes £179 profit for each burglar alarm sold and £23 for each spotlight. How much money will she make in total during this month?

Use a calculator for this exercise.

1 Copy and complete this multiplication square.

×		$\frac{1}{5}$	$2\frac{1}{4}$		
	$\frac{1}{2}$				
$1\frac{1}{3}$					
$\frac{7}{9}$	$\frac{14}{27}$			$\frac{35}{54}$	
		$\frac{4}{25}$			$\frac{2}{5}$
					$\frac{1}{3}$

2 Alana watches two films, one after the other. The first film lasts $1\frac{2}{3}$ hours and the second film lasts $2\frac{1}{10}$ hours. What is the total running time of both films?

3 A piece of timber is $3\frac{1}{4}$ m long. Terry uses two-thirds of the piece of timber. What length of timber does Terry use?

4 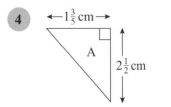 Which shape has the larger area and by how much?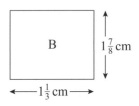

5 Liz needs to work out $\frac{2}{5} + 3$ on her calculator. She gets the answer $\frac{1}{4}$.

Explain clearly what she has typed to get this incorrect answer.

6 Work out

a $\frac{2}{3} \times \left(\frac{3}{4} - \frac{1}{5}\right)$

b $\frac{9}{10} \div \left(\frac{3}{5} - \frac{3}{20}\right)$

c $\frac{5}{7} \times \left(2\frac{1}{4} - \frac{7}{8}\right)$

d $\left(3\frac{1}{2}\right)^2 + \frac{5}{6}$

e $4\frac{1}{4} \div 1\frac{1}{2} + \frac{5}{9}$

f $\dfrac{2\frac{1}{2} + 3\frac{2}{5}}{1\frac{1}{5} - \frac{5}{6}}$

Work out the following. Give each answer correct to one decimal place where appropriate.

1 $-9 \div (-2)$ **2** $-18 - 14$ **3** $-6.2 \times (-3.1)$ **4** $4.8 - (-3.72)$

5 $-46 \div 4.13$ **6** $(-8.12)^2$ **7** $\dfrac{(-7) \times 2}{-5}$ **8** $9 - 4.6^2$

9 $\dfrac{8 - (-0.17)}{2.3}$ **10** $\left(\dfrac{-3.6}{1.92}\right) - (-2.8)$ **11** $(-7.2 - 3.93)^2$ **12** $49 - (-4.6)^2$

13 Copy and complete

    a $-3.7 + \boxed{} = 12.1$ **b** $5.17 + \boxed{} = -11.03$

    c $\dfrac{-12.48}{\boxed{}} = -2.6$ **d** $4.3 \times \boxed{} = -29.24$

14 Which calculation gives the larger answer and by how much?

    A $\boxed{(-4.9)^2 + 4.52}$ B $\boxed{(-5.2 + 10.31)^2 - 2.06}$

15 Which calculation gives the larger answer and by how much?

    A $\boxed{\sqrt{(4.1 - (-8.15))}}$ B $\boxed{\dfrac{4.16 + (-1.9)^2}{2}}$

3.5 Fractions, decimals and percentages

1 Answer 'true' or 'false'.

    a $0.03 = \dfrac{3}{100}$ **b** $\dfrac{3}{5} = 0.35$ **c** $\dfrac{17}{20} = 0.85$

    d $0.34 = \dfrac{3}{4}$ **e** $\dfrac{70}{100} = 0.7$ **f** $\dfrac{8}{25} = 0.32$

2 Change the following decimals to fractions, cancelling when possible.

    a 0.2   **b** 0.09   **c** 0.36   **d** 0.75   **e** 0.007

    f 0.025   **g** 0.73   **h** 0.008   **i** 0.45   **j** 0.16

3 Change the following fractions to decimals.

a $\frac{2}{5}$ b $\frac{11}{20}$ c $\frac{19}{50}$ d $\frac{13}{25}$ e $\frac{1}{8}$

4 Carl spends 0.7 of his money. What fraction of his money does he have left?

5 Wendy has painted 0.55 of her living room. What fraction of her living room is not painted?

6 For each pair of numbers, write down which is the larger.

a $\frac{7}{10}$ 0.8   b 0.94 $\frac{19}{20}$ c 0.17 $\frac{3}{20}$

d 0.26 $\frac{7}{25}$ e $\frac{3}{50}$ 0.04   f $\frac{9}{25}$ 0.49

7 Milo says that $\frac{2}{5}$ is greater than 0.5. Is this true or false? Justify your answer.

8 Write in order of size, largest first.

0.3   0.29 $\frac{1}{4}$ 0.32 $\frac{7}{25}$

HWK 2M   **Main Book page 203**

1
$\frac{7}{20}$ $\frac{6}{25}$ $\frac{9}{40}$ $\frac{1}{4}$

Change each fraction to a percentage, then write these fractions in order of size, starting with the smallest.

2 Change these percentages to fractions.

a 41%   b 24%   c 6%   d 45%   e 32%

3 Change these percentages to decimals.

a 3%   b 30%   c 16%   d 75%   e 85%

4

Some people were asked what their favourite Disney cartoon was. The pie chart shows the results.

a What percentage prefer Snow White?

b What percentage prefer Jungle Book?

c What is the difference between the percentages for Jungle Book and the Lion King?

d What percentage prefer 'others'?

5 Change these decimals to percentages.

a 0.33   **b** 0.64   **c** 0.09   **d** 0.14   **e** 1.3

6 36% of people asked said they did not vote at the last General Election. What *fraction* of the people asked did vote at the last General Election?

7

80%	$\frac{12}{150}$	26%	$\frac{4}{5}$	16%	0.65	$\frac{15}{40}$	75%	$\frac{3}{25}$
0.48								0.08
0.75								$\frac{16}{20}$
$\frac{12}{25}$								$\frac{3}{8}$
$\frac{13}{20}$								65%
0.34								$\frac{21}{28}$
$\frac{13}{50}$								$\frac{2}{25}$
37.5%								$\frac{39}{150}$
0.26	$\frac{36}{75}$	$\frac{12}{65}$	8%	$\frac{3}{4}$	0.8	48%	$\frac{52}{80}$	0.375

Each number belongs to a group of four equivalent numbers (two fractions, one decimal and one percentage).

Write down each group of four numbers.

Beware: there are four numbers which do *not* belong to any group.

74

Change the following fractions to recurring decimals by dividing.

1 $\dfrac{1}{9}$ **2** $\dfrac{2}{7}$ **3** $\dfrac{1}{3}$ **4** $\dfrac{4}{7}$ **5** $\dfrac{1}{11}$

6 $\dfrac{6}{7}$ **7** $\dfrac{8}{9}$ **8** $\dfrac{4}{33}$ **9** $\dfrac{4}{11}$ **10** $\dfrac{2}{99}$

11 Which fraction below is 0.81818181…?

$\left(\dfrac{10}{13}\right)$ $\left(\dfrac{9}{11}\right)$ $\left(\dfrac{5}{7}\right)$

3.6 Brackets and equations

In questions **1** to **6** , answer 'true' or 'false'.

1 $3(x + 2) = 3x + 5$ **2** $5(x - 4) = 5x - 20$ **3** $2(4x + 3) = 14x$

4 $6(2x - 1) = 11x$ **5** $4(2x + 7) = 8x + 28$ **6** $3(2x - 1) = 6x - 3$

Expand (multiply out) the following expressions.

7 $6(x - 2)$ **8** $2(4x + 9)$ **9** $5(3x + 2)$

10 $x(m + n)$ **11** $y(a - b)$ **12** $m(n - 4)$

13 $p(m + 3)$ **14** $5(b + c)$ **15** $x(y - b)$

16 $a(b - c)$ **17** $x(3y + 2)$ **18** $a(a + 3)$

19 $x(x - 7)$ **20** $n(4 + n)$ **21** $4(2p - 1)$

22 Copy and complete

    a $4(3x - \square) = 12x - 8$ **b** $7(\square + 3p) = 42 + 21p$

    c $3(\square - \square) = 15a - 24$ **d** $\square(4 + \square) = 20 + 35n$

23 Write down an expression for the area of this rectangle.

Remove the brackets and simplify.

1 $4(x + 3) + 2(x + 5)$

2 $5(x + 1) + 7(x + 3)$

3 $7(x + 4) + 6(x + 2)$

4 $8(x + 3) + 4(x + 6)$

5 $6(2x + 3) + 2(x + 7)$

6 $3(3x + 2) + 5(2x + 7)$

7 $4(3x + 1) + 3(5x + 2)$

8 $7(4x + 2) + 2(8x + 3)$

9 $9(x + 3) + 5(4x + 5)$

10 $6x + 3(2x + 1)$

11 $3 + 8(4x + 1)$

12 $5(3x + 2) + 7x$

13

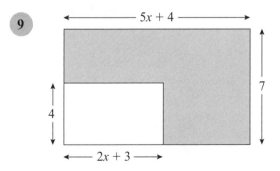

3

5

$x + 4$

$2x + 1$

Write down an expression for the sum of the areas of these two rectangles. Simplify your answer.

14   Simplify $4(3x + 1) + 2(2x + 6) + 7(x + 8)$

15   Simplify $3(5x + 4) + 4(2 + 8x) + 8(2x + 5) + 2(1 + 7x)$

Remove the brackets and simplify.

1 $3(x + 4) + 2(x - 3)$

2 $5(2x + 3) + 3(x - 2)$

3 $4(2x + 6) + 3(4x - 5)$

4 $5(3x + 4) - 4(2x - 3)$

5 $6(2x - 1) + 5(3x + 2)$

6 $7(2x + 3) - 5(x + 3)$

7 $8(4x + 7) - 4(3x + 8)$

8 $6(5x + 9) - 2(10x - 1)$

9

$5x + 4$

7

4

$2x + 3$

Write down an expression for the shaded area. Simplify your answer.

Remove the brackets and simplify.

10 $4(2a + 5b) - 5(a + 2b)$

11 $6(3a + b) - 4(2a - 3b)$

12 $5(4x + 3y) - 2(2x + y)$

13 $9(2m + 3n) - 6(m + 4n)$

14 $7(5m + 6n) - 4(7m - 3n)$

15 $5(2x + 9y) - 6(x + 5y)$

HWK 3M | **Main Book page 210**

Solve

1 $m - 7 = 9$

2 $10 + y = 43$

3 $6 = x - 27$

4 $13 + n = 40$

5 $6a = 48$

6 $4y - 5 = 23$

7 $5x + 8 = 23$

8 $4y - 15 = 21$

9 $5p + 9 = 39$

10 $8c - 17 = 15$

11 $6m - 30 = 42$

12 $3n + 23 = 38$

Solve

13 $4a + 16 = 36$

14 $9y - 13 = 59$

15 $8x - 6 = 2$

16 $6n - 85 = 35$

17 $10m + 26 = 26$

18 $60 = 7y + 39$

19 $21 = 4m - 23$

20 $23 = 8x + 7$

21 $7p - 49 = 7$

Solve

22 $\frac{a}{6} = 4$

23 $\frac{m}{9} = 3$

24 $\frac{x}{10} = 7$

25 $\frac{n}{4} = 8$

26 $\frac{w}{3} = 13$

27 $6 = \frac{n}{7}$

28 $\frac{m}{2} + 1 = 4$

29 $\frac{a}{5} - 3 = 2$

30 $\frac{w}{8} + 6 = 10$

HWK 4M | **Main Book page 211**

Solve

1 $5n + 6 = 2n + 33$

2 $8x - 4 = 3x + 21$

3 $6p + 10 = 4p + 16$

4 $9a + 16 = 5a + 48$

5 $7y - 3 = 4y + 18$

6 $6x - 10 = x + 40$

7 $4m + 7 = 2m + 11$

8 $10a - 12 = 5a + 18$

9 $6y - 32 = 2y + 28$

10 $8x + 13 = 6x + 23$

11 $10m + 14 = 6m + 66$

12 $5p - 27 = 2p + 33$

13

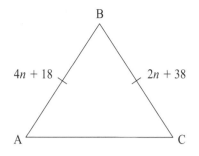

The sides AB and BC are equal.

Find the value of n, then write down the length of side AB, assuming all values are in cm.

Solve

14 $2 + 5x = x + 42$ **15** $9y - 12 = 3y$ **16** $4n = 3n + 45$

17 $7p - 22 = 2p + 18$ **18** $11 + 6a = 9a - 16$ **19** $8m - 28 = m$

HWK 5M	Main Book page 212

Solve

1 $3(n + 5) = 36$ **2** $6(n + 2) = 24$ **3** $8(n - 3) = 40$

4 $7(2n - 3) = 49$ **5** $4(2n + 1) = 36$ **6** $10(n - 6) = 30$

7 $2(3n + 6) = 30$ **8** $5(n - 7) = 15$ **9** $3(2n - 3) = 27$

10 $4(2n - 7) = 60$ **11** $6(5n + 2) = 42$ **12** $2(n - 40) = 20$

13 Dom has £n. He spends £20. He then finds a £100 coat in a shop which costs five times the money he now has left.

    a Write down an equation involving n.   **b** Find n.

Solve

14 $4(3n + 1) = 40$ **15** $30 = 2(n + 6)$ **16** $25 = 5(2n - 3)$

17 $90 = 3(n + 10)$ **18** $7(2n - 9) = 7$ **19** $120 = 8(n + 5)$

20 The area of this triangle is 72 cm². Write down an equation, then find the value of n.

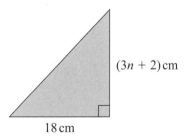

$(3n + 2)$ cm

18 cm

21 Solve

    a $10(n + 4) = 9(n + 5)$ **b** $6(n - 4) = 3(n + 2)$ **c** $6(3n - 1) = 2(5n + 5)$

78

In questions **1** to **4** , form an equation and then solve it to find the number.

1   If we multiply the number by 4 and then subtract 6, the answer is 50

2   If we double the number and add 15, the answer is 53

3   If we add 7 to the number and then double the result, the answer is 58

4   If we subtract 15 from the number and then multiply the result by 3, the answer is 48

5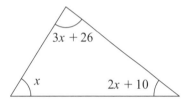

    a Form an equation involving x.
    b Solve the equation to find x.
    c Write down the value of each angle in the triangle.

6

The perimeter of this rectangle is 38 cm.
    a Form an equation involving x.
    b Solve the equation to find x.
    c Write down the values of the length and width of the rectangle.

7   Alex has £$(6n + 3)$ and Fiona has £$(3n + 15)$. If they both have the same amount of money, form an equation involving n. Solve the equation and write down how much money Fiona has.

8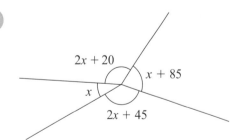

    a Form an equation involving x.
    b Solve the equation to find x.
    c Write down the value of each angle in the diagram.

9 This rectangle has an area of 120 cm². Form an equation and solve it to find x.

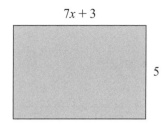

$7x + 3$

5

10

P

$3(4n + 7)$

Q

81 cm

R

PQ and QR are the equal sides in an isosceles triangle. Find the value of n.

UNIT 4

4.1 Averages and range

1 | 5 | 6 | 13 | 8 | 6 | 5 | 8 | 4 | 10 | 4 | 8 |

For the list of numbers above, find

a the mean   **b** the median   **c** the mode   **d** the range.

2 The numbers below show the scores of ten golfers.

$-3, -1, -5, +2, +3, -6, -4, -3, +2, -4$

Write down the median score.

3 Which set of numbers below has the greater range?

A | $5, -2, 9, 3, -1, 8$ | or   B | $-6, 2, -2, 5, -3, 6, -4$ |

4 Nine people have weights 52 kg, 63 kg, 51 kg, 48 kg, 62 kg, 59 kg, 60 kg, 62 kg and 56 kg.

a Find the mean weight of the nine people.

b Two more people join the group. They weigh 79 kg each. Find the mean weight of all 11 people.

5 | 3 | 7 | ? | 10 |

The numbers on these cards have a mean average equal to 6.
Write down the missing number.

6 The numbers 7, 4, 9, 2, 7 and n have a median equal to 6. Write down the value of n.

7 Nine children get the following marks in a test:

36, 50, 54, 59, 37, 62, 52, 51, 49

Gemma scored the mean average mark. Was she in the bottom half or the top half of this list of marks?

8 Set A: | 8 | 10 | 5 | 9 | 6 | 7 | 4 |

Set B: | 12 | 1 | ? | 8 | 9 |

The mean average of set B is the same as the mean average of set A.
Find the missing number.

9 The six numbers below are all positive and have a range of 39. Find the value of *n*.

$(15)\ (21)\ (3)\ (n)\ (32)\ (9)$

10 Seven numbers have a mean of 9 and a median of 8

6	6	15	15			

Write down three possible missing numbers.

HWK 2M ——————————————————— **Main Book page 234**

1 Children in class 8A are given a maths test. Their marks are recorded below.

17	23	19	28	15	17	22	28	19	20
24	8	21	15	28	16	27	29	21	23

a Find the mean mark and the range of the marks.

b Children in class 8B took the same test. Their mean mark was 24 and the range of the marks was 12. Use the means and the ranges to compare the test marks for classes 8A and 8B.

2

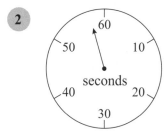

Two groups of people were asked to estimate when one minute had passed. Their estimates are shown in the boxes below. The times are given in seconds.

Group X	54	61	60	55	62	66	61	51	52

Group Y	59	58	67	50	63	69	71	67

a Work out the mean estimate and the range for group X.

b Work out the mean estimate and the range for group Y.

c Write one or two sentences to compare the estimates for the two groups.

You may use a calculator

1 The frequency table shows the weights of 50 apples in a box.

Weight	90 g	100 g	110 g	120 g	130 g
Frequency	8	11	17	9	5

   a Calculate the mean weight of the apples.

   b Find the modal weight of the apples (i.e. the mode).

2 40 children were asked how many drinks of water they had during one day. The findings are shown in the frequency table below.

Number of drinks	0	1	2	3	4	5	6
Frequency	3	5	6	7	12	5	2

   a Calculate the mean number of drinks.

   b Find the modal number of drinks (i.e. the mode).

3 Tom wants to know if a 'city' family or a 'village' family spends more or less each week on food. He asks 25 families in a city and 25 families in a village to share their weekly food bill. The results are shown in the frequency tables below.

City	
Food bill (£)	Frequency
80	0
100	4
120	8
140	6
160	7

Village	
Food bill (£)	Frequency
80	5
100	5
120	10
140	4
160	1

   a Calculate the mean weekly food bill for the 'city' families.

   b Calculate the mean weekly food bill for the 'village' families.

   c Which group of families spends more each week on food? Can you suggest a possible reason for this?

4.2 Charts, including scatter graphs

1 The scatter graph shows the waist sizes and weights of some people.

   a How many people weighed more than 70 kg?

   b How many people had a waist size of less than 36 inches?

   c Answer *true* or *false*: 'In general as waist size increases, weight increases.'

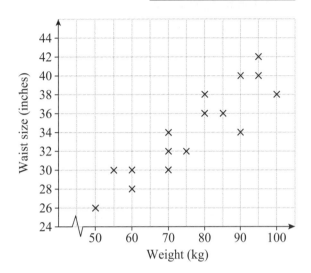

2 The scatter graph shows the heights of some people and how many shirts they own.

   a How many people are more than 150 cm tall?

   b How many people own fewer than 8 shirts?

   c Answer *true* or *false*: 'In general as the number of shirts increases, height increases.'

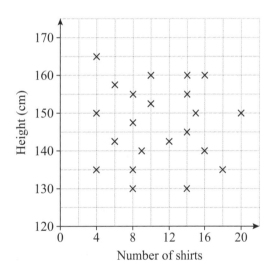

3

French test	German test
13	14
19	17
16	17
8	8
16	15
3	4
10	11
20	19
18	18
7	5
11	12
18	19
10	8
12	10
9	9
15	16

The table shows two test scores obtained by 16 children in Year 8 for French and German.

a Draw the axes shown below and complete the scatter graph.

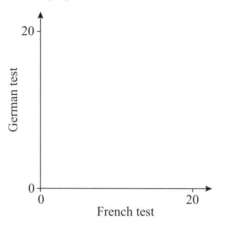

b What is the connection in general between the French and German test marks?

4 Describe the correlation, if any, in these scatter graphs.

a
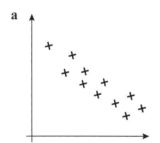

b
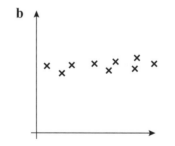

c
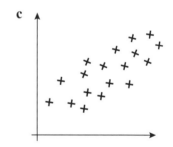

1 The table below shows the expected crowd size, the cost of a ticket and the number of goals expected at the next match for three football teams.

Team	Crowd size	Ticket cost (£)	Number of goals
Chelsea	43 000	52	2
Manchester United	72 000	60	3
Aston Villa	54 000	45	2

a Which team has the highest ticket cost?

b Which team expects the highest number of goals in the next match?

c Which team will have the lowest crowd size?

2 The hair colour of children in a primary school is recorded in the table below.

	Dark hair	Blond hair	Other colours
Boys	43	39	16
Girls	32	51	19

a How many girls have dark hair?

b How many children in total have blond hair?

c How many girls are there in the primary school?

d What percentage of the boys have dark hair? Give the answer to one decimal place.

e What fraction of the children have dark hair?

3

Name	Weekly hours in July	Weekly hours in January
Mark	84	28
Amy	73	21
Gwyn	79	40
Tasha	72	14

Mark, Amy, Gwyn and Tasha work in restaurants in a seaside town.

The table shows the number of hours they work each week in July and January.

a Who worked the most weekly hours in July?

b How many hours more did Tasha work each week in July than January?

c How many hours less than Gwyn did Amy work each week in July?

4   The table opposite shows the cost per mile for a petrol car and a diesel car.

Petrol	12.5p per mile
Diesel	8p per mile

The next table shows the road distances in miles between various cities.

a Ugo drives a petrol car from Liverpool to Birmingham. How much money does he spend on the petrol?

b Chloe drives a diesel car from Leeds to Newcastle. How much money does she spend on diesel?

c Ugo now drives from Birmingham to Sheffield to Newcastle, then back to Birmingham again. How much money does he spend on petrol for this complete round trip?

Leeds

30	Sheffield

64	63	Liverpool

87	117	151	Newcastle

105	75	86	192	Birmingham

HWK 4M ——————————————————————————— **Main Book page 245**

1   The weights (in kg) of 24 people are recorded below.

64	81	78	57	86	70
69	70	94	77	52	72
92	66	61	87	78	63
81	78	57	66	80	72

Remember the key, for example: 6|4 means 64 kg

Draw an ordered stem and leaf diagram.
Three entries are shown below.

Stem	Leaf
5	
6	4 9
7	
8	1
9	

2   The heights of two groups of teenagers are measured. The heights for each group are shown in the frequency diagrams below.

Group A

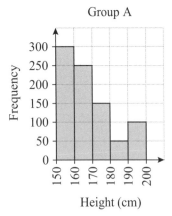

Group B

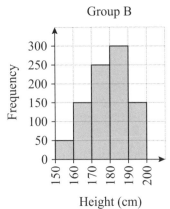

a Which group of teenagers is generally taller?

b Which frequency diagram would you expect if you measured the heights of all the teenagers in a Sixth Form College? Explain your answer.

3 **a** Eighteen 10-year-old children run a 400 metre race. Their times t (in seconds) are shown below.

64, 63, 86, 75, 81, 92, 74, 77, 85,

93, 76, 65, 84, 91, 73, 83, 76, 75

Put the times into groups.

Class interval	Frequency
$60 \leqslant t < 70$	
$70 \leqslant t < 80$	
$80 \leqslant t < 90$	
$90 \leqslant t < 100$	

b Draw a frequency diagram like those in question **2**.

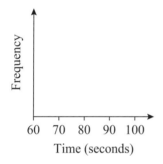

c The same children run a 400 metre race when they are 17 years old. Their times t (in seconds) are shown below.

67, 56, 65, 57, 53, 74, 59, 53, 71,

68, 52, 66, 75, 61, 54, 62, 56, 63

Put the times into groups similar to part **a**.

d Draw a frequency diagram like those in question **2**.

e Write a sentence to compare the times shown by each frequency diagram. Suggest a reason for the difference.

4 A group of children are measuring the lengths of leaves for a biology experiment.
The stem and leaf diagram opposite shows the length of each leaf.

a What is the median length of a leaf?

b What percentage of the leaves are greater than 7.5 cm in length?

Stem	Leaf
5	2 3 7 7
6	0 1 1 4 8 9
7	0 0 2 3 3 7 7 7
8	1 5 5 7 8
9	0 2 4

Key   7|3 means 7.3 cm

1   72 people were asked what their favourite type of chocolate was. The results are shown in the table below.

Type of chocolate	Frequency
milk	32
dark	30
white	10

    a Work out the angle on a pie chart for one person (i.e. 360° ÷ total number of people).

    b Work out the angle for each type of chocolate and draw a pie chart.

2   Some people are asked to name their favourite European capital city. The results are shown in the table opposite. Draw an accurate pie chart to show this information.

Capital city	Frequency
Paris	6
Rome	6
London	8
Berlin	1
Madrid	3

3

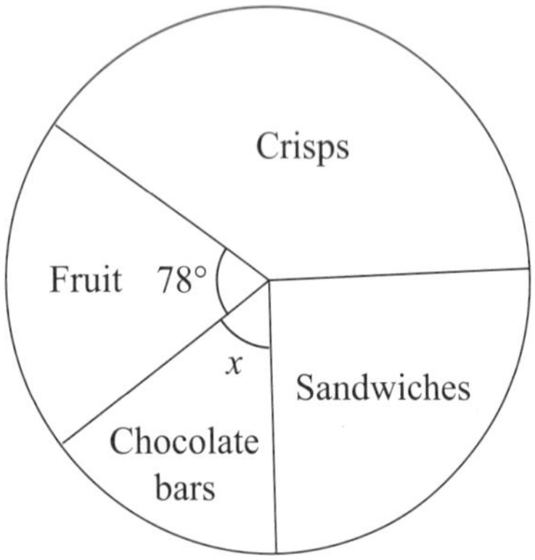

Year 8 children who bring packed lunches to school are asked what main items they have in their lunch box. The pie chart opposite shows the results.

40% of items are crisps and $\frac{1}{4}$ are sandwiches.

Calculate the size of angle x in the pie chart.

4   A garage records the type of vehicle stopping for petrol one day. The results are shown in the table opposite.

Find the angle on a pie chart for each type of vehicle, then draw the pie chart.

Type of vehicle	Percentage
car	50%
van	20%
motorbike	15%
lorry	10%
other	5%

5 900 pupils in Cork Field School and 350 pupils in Manor High School were asked what they enjoyed doing most at weekends. The results are shown in the two pie charts.

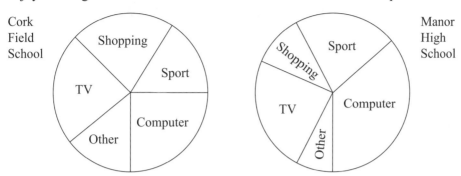

Cork Field School

Manor High School

Did more pupils in Manor High School choose using the computer than pupils in Cork Field School or less? *Explain* your answer.

4.3 Pythagoras' theorem

HWK 1M ——————————————————————— **Main Book page 256**

Use Pythagoras' theorem in this exercise and give answers correct to two decimal places. The units are cm.

1 Find the value of *x* in each triangle.

a
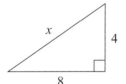

b
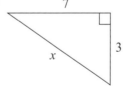

c
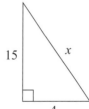

2 Find the value of *x* in each triangle.

a
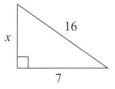

b
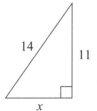

c
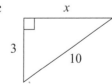

90

3 Find the side marked with a letter.

a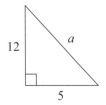

b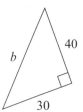

c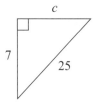

d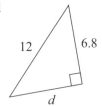

e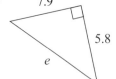

f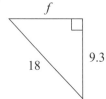

g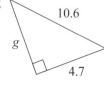

h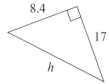

HWK 2M ──────────────────────────── **Main Book page 258**

Give all answers to two decimal places if required.

1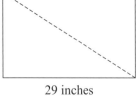

Calculate the length of the diagonal of this rectangular TV screen.

2 A ladder of length 4 m rests against a vertical wall. The bottom of the ladder is 1.8 m from the wall. How far up the wall does the ladder reach?

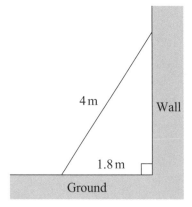

3 A balloon flies 25 miles north and then a further 18 miles west. How far is the balloon from its starting point?

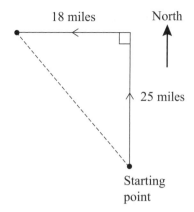

18 miles

North

25 miles

Starting point

4 A plane flies 30 km south and then a further 27 km east. The plane then flies directly back to its starting point. How far does the plane fly in total?

5 A ladder of length 6 m rests against a vertical wall, with its foot 2.3 m from the wall. Will the ladder reach a window which is 5.5 m above the ground? *Explain* your answer.

6 George travels to school from home via the shop. His sister, Rosie, travels directly from home to school. How much further does George travel compared with Rosie?

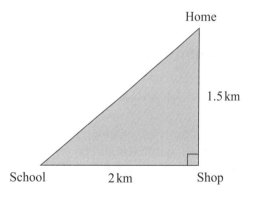

Home

1.5 km

School   2 km   Shop

7

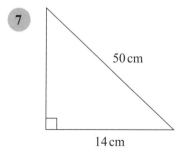

50 cm

14 cm

Calculate the area of this triangle.

92

8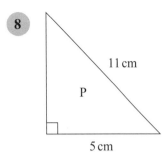

Which triangle has the greater perimeter and by how much?

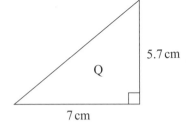

9 Work out the lengths of x and y opposite.

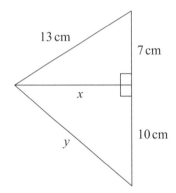

4.4 Bearings and scale drawing

HWK 1M   **Main Book page 265**

1 Ten police officers are searching for a stolen car. They all set off in different directions, as shown. On what bearing does each police officer travel?

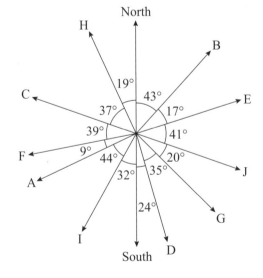

2

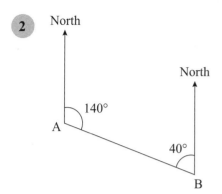

a Write down the bearing of B from A.

b Write down the bearing of A from B.

3 Measure the bearing of   **a** A to B   **b** C to D   **c** E to F   **d** G to H

                                   e I to J   **f** K to L   **g** M to N

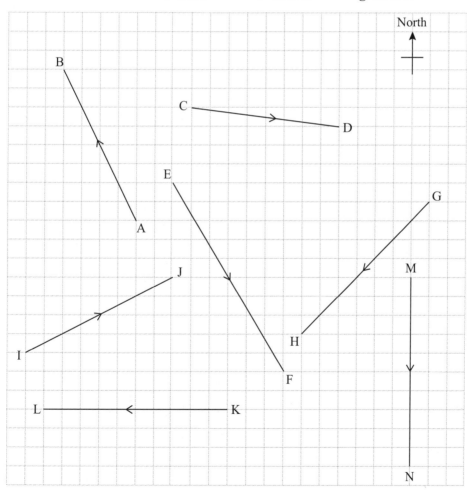

4

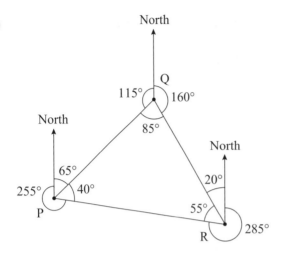

Write down the bearing of

a Q from P

b R from Q

c R from P

d P from R

5 A ship sails from A to P, then to B. Another ship sails from C to Q, then to D.

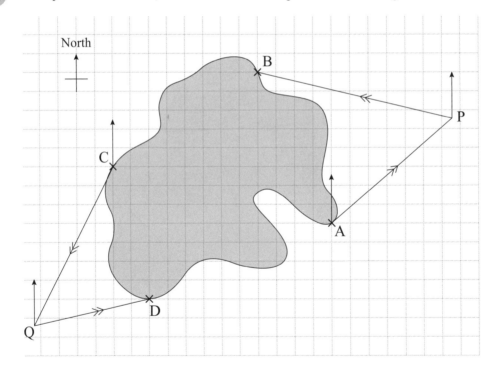

a Measure the bearing of A to P.

b Measure the bearing of P to B.

c Measure the bearing of C to Q.

d Measure the bearing of Q to D.

Draw an accurate scale drawing of each shape below using the scale shown.

1

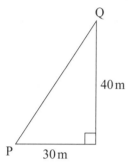

Use 1 cm for every 10 m. Measure and write down the real length of PQ (in metres).

2

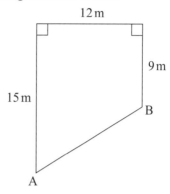

Use 1 cm for every 3 m. Measure and write down the real length of AB (in metres).

3

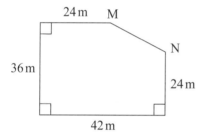

Use 1 cm for every 6 m. Measure and write down the real length of MN (in metres).

4 Choose a room in your house.
  a Measure the longest length and write it down.
  b Choose a sensible scale and write it down.
  c Make an accurate scale drawing of the room.

In questions **1** to **6**, use a scale of 1 cm to represent 1 km. Make an accurate scale drawing to help you answer each question.

1 A ship sails 7 km due north and then a further 5 km on a bearing of 075°. How far is the ship now from its starting point?

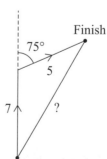

2 A ship sails 6 km due north and then a further 6 km on a bearing of 080°. How far is the ship now from its starting point?

3 A man walks 8 km due west and then a further 5 km due south. How far is the man now from his starting point?

4 Sarah and Barclay are standing at the same point A. Sarah walks for 7 km on a bearing of 050°. Barclay walks for 6 km on a bearing of 310°. How far is Sarah from Barclay now?

5 A ship sails due south for 6 km and then on a bearing of 120° for 3 km. How far is the ship now from its starting point?

6 Draw a point P with a cross. Point Q is 7 km from P on a bearing of 072° from P.
Point R is 5 km from P on a bearing of 190° from P. What is the bearing of R from Q?

4.5 Congruent shapes and tessellation

HWK 1M ———————————————————— **Main Book page 273**

1 Decide which shapes are congruent pairs. (You can use tracing paper.)

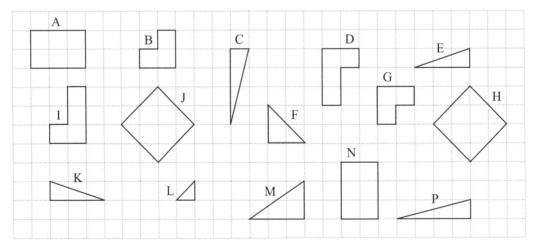

2 Draw a pentagon (5-sided shape) then draw a congruent pentagon.

3 Draw a hexagon (6-sided shape) then draw a congruent hexagon.

4

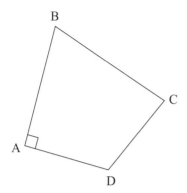

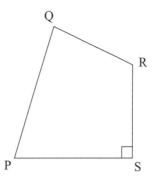

The two shapes above are congruent. Sam says that side AD is equal to side SR.
Is Sam correct?

5 Draw and colour a design which uses at least three different types of congruent shapes.

HWK 2M ──────────────────── **Main Book page 275**

1 Draw any quadrilateral (4-sided shape) on paper or card and cut it out. Use this template to draw a tessellation. Colour in your pattern.

2 Draw another tessellation pattern using at least two different shapes. Colour in your pattern. An example is shown opposite.

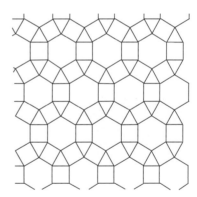

4.6 Negative numbers

HWK 1M ──────────────────── **Main Book page 277**

$$-6 \quad -5 \quad -4 \quad -3 \quad -2 \quad -1 \quad 0 \quad 1 \quad 2 \quad 3 \quad 4 \quad 5 \quad 6$$

1 Answer 'true' or 'false'.

a $4 - 7 = -3$ **b** $-4 + 1 = -5$ **c** $-5 - 1 = -4$

d $-4 - 2 = -6$ **e** $-6 + 4 = -2$ **f** $-3 + 7 = -10$

2 Copy and complete this number chain.

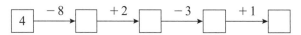

3 Work out

a $-1 - 4$ b $-3 - 5$ c $-6 + 5$ d $-2 + 6$

e $3 - 8$ f $-6 - 3$ g $-7 + 2$ h $-4 + 4$

4 Which calculation below gives the odd answer out?

A $\boxed{-5 + 2}$ B $\boxed{-2 - 2}$ C $\boxed{-9 + 5}$

5 Copy and fill in the missing numbers.

a $-3 - \boxed{} = -4$ b $6 - \boxed{} = -3$ c $-7 + \boxed{} = 1$

6 Six judges in a dance competition give the following scores:

$\boxed{+3}$ $\boxed{-1}$ $\boxed{-2}$ $\boxed{+1}$ $\boxed{+5}$ $\boxed{-2}$

What is the total score given by these judges?

7 Use a number line to *explain clearly* why $-5 - 3$ is *not* -2

8 What is the value of m if $m + m + m = -12$?

9 Jacob has four cards, as shown below.

$\boxed{-6}$ $\boxed{-2}$ $\boxed{3}$ $\boxed{1}$

He needs to choose one more card to make the total of all five cards equal to -5.
Draw the card he needs.

HWK 2M ——————————————————— **Main Book page 277**

1 Answer 'true' or 'false'.

a $7 + (-3) = 4$ b $3 - (-1) = 2$ c $7 - (-2) = 5$

d $3 - (+2) = 5$ e $7 + (-5) = 2$ f $5 - (-3) = 8$

2 Copy and complete this number chain.

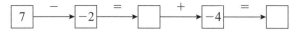

3 Work out

   a $8 - (+3)$ **b** $6 + (-5)$ **c** $1 + (-3)$ **d** $5 - (-4)$

   e $4 - (-1)$ **f** $7 + (-6)$ **g** $-3 - (-2)$ **h** $-2 + (-4)$

4 What is the difference between -19 and 1?

5 What is the sum of -1, -2 and -3?

6 Copy and fill in the missing numbers.

   a $-2 - \square = 1$ **b** $5 - \square = 6$ **c** $-3 + \square = -7$

7 Which calculation below gives the odd answer out?

   A $\boxed{-4 + (-1)}$ B $\boxed{-3 - (-1)}$ C $\boxed{3 + (-5)}$

8 Gregor says that $-1 - (-3) = -1 + 3 = -4$.
   Is he correct? Give reasons for your answer.

9 Work out

   a $-6 + (-2) - (-4)$ **b** $-9 - (-7) - 2$

   c $-3 - (-4) - (-1) - 6 + (-4)$ **d** $-5 - 2 + (-3) - (-6) - 2$

   e $1 + (-4) - (-2) - 4 + (-3) - (-6)$

10 Complete this 'magic square'. (You must get the same number when you add across each row, add down each column and add diagonally.)

-2	-3	
	-1	
	1	

HWK 3M ┤   **Main Book page 280**

1 Work out

   a $4 \times (-3)$ **b** $-2 \times (-6)$ **c** $-8 \times (-3)$ **d** -7×2

   e $-5 \times (-2)$ **f** $2 \times (-9)$ **g** $6 \times (-6)$ **h** $-4 \times (-1)$

   i $-7 \times (-6)$ **j** $-3 \times (-9)$ **k** $10 \times (-4)$ **l** -20×3

2 The temperature in Glasgow is $-4°C$. The temperature in Toronto is six times as cold. What is the temperature in Toronto?

3 Which question below gives the highest answer and by how much?

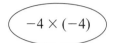   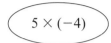

4 Copy and complete this number chain.

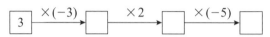

5 Copy and complete these calculations.

a $-6 \times \Box = -30$ **b** $9 \times \Box = -36$ **c** $-10 \times \Box = 70$

d $\Box \times (-2) = -14$ **e** $-8 \times \Box = 32$ **f** $\Box \times (-8) = 48$

6 Find the value of mn if $m = -4$ and $n = -6$

7 Find the value of p^2 if $p = -3$

8 Find the value of $3m + n$ if $m = -7$ and $n = 10$

9 Find the value of abc if $a = 4$, $b = -6$ and $c = -2$

10 What number belongs in the empty box if $-8 + 3 \times \Box = -14$?

HWK 4M   **Main Book page 280**

1 Work out

a $8 \div (-2)$ **b** $-20 \div (-5)$ **c** $-28 \div (-7)$ **d** $40 \div (-5)$

e $-32 \div 8$ **f** $-45 \div (-9)$ **g** $56 \div (-8)$ **h** $-16 \div 8$

i $60 \div (-5)$ **j** $-36 \div 9$ **k** $63 \div (-9)$ **l** $-100 \div 20$

2 -32 is divided by each number below. Write down which of these numbers will give an answer greater than zero.

$\boxed{4}$ $\boxed{-8}$ $\boxed{-2}$ $\boxed{16}$ $\boxed{32}$

3 Answer 'true' or 'false'.

a $-3 \times (-3) = -9$ **b** $(-3)^2 = 9$ **c** $-5 \times (-4) = 20$

d $2 \times (-3) \times (-4) = 24$ **e** $(-5)^2 = 10$ **f** $-1 \times (-1) \times (-1) = -1$

4 Copy and complete each number chain.

a

-2 →$\times 5$→ ☐ →$\div 2$→ ☐ →$\times(-4)$→ ☐ →$\div(-10)$→ ☐

b

☐ →$\times 4$→ ☐ →$\div(-8)$→ ☐ →$\times 9$→ ☐ →$\div(-3)$→ -6

5 Copy and fill in the empty boxes.

a $-4 \times$ ☐ $= 40$ b $9 \times$ ☐ $= -36$ c ☐ $\div (-4) = -7$

d ☐ $\times 6 = -30$ e $-8 \div$ ☐ $= -2$ f ☐ $\div (-9) = 5$

6 Work out

a $-5 \times (-4) \div 2 \times (-3)$

b $-30 \div (-6) \times 4 \div (-2)$

c $50 \div (-5) \div 2 \times (-8) \div (-10)$

7 Copy and complete this multiplication square.

$\times$	-5		
		-9	6
4			-8
	35		

8 Find two numbers that multiply to give -28 and add together to make -3

UNIT 5

5.1 Sequences 2

1   Look at the sequence 5, 8, 11, 14, …

The *difference* between the terms is 3

Copy the table which has a column for $3n$.

Copy and complete:

'The nth term of the sequence is $3n + \square$.'

n	$3n$	Term
1	3	5
2	6	8
3	9	11
4	12	14

2   Look at each sequence and the table underneath.

Find the nth term in each case.

a Sequence 8, 13, 18, 23, …

n	$5n$	Term
1	5	8
2	10	13
3	$\square$	18
4	$\square$	23

nth term = $\boxed{}$

b Sequence 2, 6, 10, 14, …

n	$4n$	Term
1	4	2
2	$\square$	6
3	$\square$	10
4	$\square$	14

nth term = $\boxed{}$

3   Look at the sequence 5, 7, 9, 11, …

Write down the *difference* between the terms.

Make a table like those in question **2** and use it to find the nth term.

4   Copy and complete

a 8, 11, 14, 17, … nth term $= 3n + \square$

b 11, 13, 15, 17, … nth term $= 2n + \square$

c 1, 6, 11, 16, … nth term $= 5n - \square$

d 3, 13, 23, 33, … nth term $= 10n - \square$

5   Write down each sequence in a table and then find the nth term.

a 2, 8, 14, 20, …   **b** 10, 13, 16, 19, …   **c** 13, 22, 31, 40, …

d 7, 17, 27, 37, …   **e** 5, 12, 19, 26, …

6 | $4n - 1$ | $n + 4$ | $2n$ | $n - 1$ | $3n + 2$ | $4n$ |

Write down each sequence below and match it to the correct expression for the nth term shown above.

a 4, 8, 12, 16, …   **b** 3, 7, 11, 15, …   **c** 0, 1, 2, 3, 4, …   **d** 5, 6, 7, 8, 9, …

HWK 2M ──────────────────────────── **Main Book page 301**

1   Callum is on the beach collecting shells.

After 1 hour he has collected 15 shells.

After 2 hours he has 25 shells.

After 3 hours he has 35 shells.

After 4 hours he has 45 shells.

a How many shells do you expect Callum to have after 5 hours?

b Answer *true* or *false*. 'After n hours, Callum will have $(15n + 10)$ shells.'

2   One fence panel has 4 vertical strips of wood
(each vertical line represents a strip of wood).

Two fence panels joined together as shown
have 7 vertical strips.

Three fence panels joined together are shown.

a How many vertical strips do 3 fence panels have?

b Draw 4 fence panels joined together.

c How many vertical strips do 4 fence panels have?

d How many vertical strips do 5 fence panels have?

e Copy and fill in the empty box:

'The number of vertical strips for n fence panels is $3n + \square$.'

In questions **3** to **7**, you are given a sequence of shapes made from sticks or dots.

If you need to, make a table to help you find the nth term of the sequence.

3   A pattern of sticks is made as shown below.

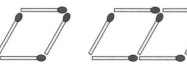

| Shape number: | $n = 1$ | $n = 2$ | $n = 3$ |
| Number of sticks: | 4 | 7 | 10 |

Draw shape number 4 and shape number 5. How many sticks are there in the nth term?

4 Here is a pattern made with dots.

Shape number:	$n = 1$	$n = 2$	$n = 3$
Number of dots:	3	5	7

Draw the next diagram in the sequence. How many dots are there in the nth term?

5 Here is another pattern made with dots.

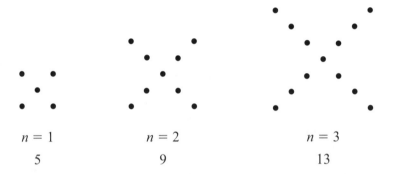

Shape number:	$n = 1$	$n = 2$	$n = 3$
Number of dots:	5	9	13

Draw the next diagram in the sequence. How many dots are there in the nth term?

6 Here is a sequence of hexagons made from sticks.

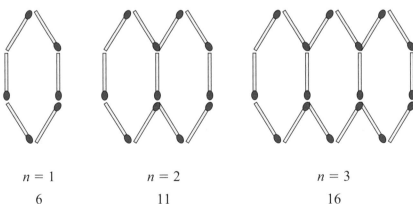

Shape number:	$n = 1$	$n = 2$	$n = 3$
Number of sticks:	6	11	16

a Draw shape number 4. How many sticks are there in the nth term?

b How many sticks are there in shape number 20?

7 Here is another pattern made with dots.

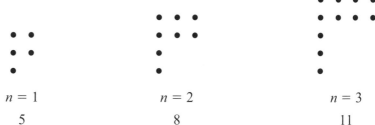

Shape number:	$n = 1$	$n = 2$	$n = 3$
Number of dots:	5	8	11

a Draw the next diagram in the sequence. How many dots are there in the nth term?

b How many dots are there in shape number 50?

5.2 More algebra

HWK 1M ———————————————————————— **Main Book page 306**

1 Simplify

a $2m \times 5n$ **b** $2n \times 2n$ **c** $7m \times 3n \times 2p$

d $6n \times 7$ **e** $\dfrac{4m}{m}$ **f** $\dfrac{3m^2}{m}$

g $3p \times 5$ **h** $7a \times 3a \times 4$ **i** $\dfrac{10ab}{5b}$

2 Isla has £20. She buys two magazines, each costing £n.
Write down an expression for how much money Isla now has.

3 The perimeter of this square is $(12n + 28)$ cm.
Write down an expression for the length of one side of the square.

?

4 Noah says that $8n + 2 = 10n$.
Explain clearly the mistake that Noah has made.

5 The number of chocolates in 3 boxes is shown.

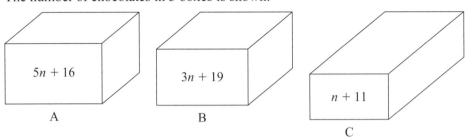

A   B   C

a $(2n + 9)$ chocolates are taken from box A. How many chocolates remain in box A?

b How many more chocolates are in box B than in box C?

c All the chocolates in boxes B and C are divided equally between 2 people.
How many chocolates does each person get?

6 A book costs £7 and a ruler costs £1. A school buys x books and y rulers.
Write down an expression for the total cost of the books and rulers.

7 How many of the statements below are true?

a $m \times m = 2m$ **b** $3x + 2y - x = 2x + 2y$

c $\dfrac{5n}{n} = 4n$ **d** $2n \times 4n = 8n^2$

e $9m - 2m + 4n - n = 7m + 4n$ **f** $\dfrac{6mn}{m} = 6n$

8 Poppy weighs n kg and Freddie weighs m kg.
Over the next 2 months, Poppy loses a kg in weight and Freddie gains b kg in weight.
If Poppy weighs more than Freddie, write down an expression for how much more
Poppy weighs than Freddie.

HWK 2M   **Main Book page 308**

1 $m = 7(4n - 1)$

Find m when $n = 6$

2 $a = \dfrac{8b - 4}{10}$

Find a when $b = 8$

3 $y = 3(9x + 2)$

Find y when $x = 2$

4 $p = \dfrac{w}{7} + 20$

Find p when $w = 28$

5 The perimeter of a rectangle is given by the formula $p = 2a + 2b$, where a is the length
and b is the width.
Find the value of p when $a = 16$ and $b = 13$

6 Gill is paid £m given by the formula $m = 8n + 42$, where n is the number of hours she works. What is the value of m if she works for 30 hours?

7 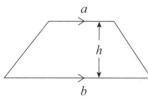 The area A of this trapezium is given by the formula

$$A = \frac{1}{2}h(a + b)$$

Find the value of A when $h = 10$, $a = 3$ and $b = 9$

8 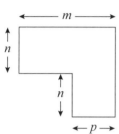 The total area A of this shape is given by the formula
$$A = n(m + p)$$
Find the value of A when $n = 20$, $m = 40$ and $p = 15$

9 In the formulae below, x is given in terms of m and n. Find the value of x in each case.

a $x = 4m + 5n$ when $m = 6$ and $n = 3$

b $x = mn + 8m$ when $m = 5$ and $n = 7$

c $x = m^2 - 4n$ when $m = 9$ and $n = 20$

10 Using the formula $I = \dfrac{PTR}{100}$, find the value of I when $P = 400$, $T = 3$ and $R = 9$.

11 This open box has no top.

The surface area A is given by the formula

$A = 2np + mn + 2mp$

Find the value of A when $m = 8$, $n = 6$ and $p = 3$

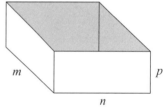

12 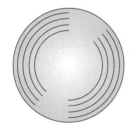 The surface area A of a sphere is approximately given by the formula

$A = 12r^2$

Find the surface area of a sphere with a radius of 4 cm

HWK 3M	Main Book page 309

1 Find the value of each expression.

a $4n - 3$ if $n = 7$ **b** $6y + 2$ if $y = 9$ **c** $8 - 2x$ if $x = 3$

d $5n - 9$ if $n = 15$ **e** $\dfrac{x}{5} + 4$ if $x = 40$ **f** $3(4 + 2y)$ if $y = 10$

g $n^2 - 19$ if $n = 8$ **h** $\dfrac{4x}{3} - 16$ if $x = 12$

2 Which of the cards below have a value of 15 when $x = 4$?

$$3x + 4$$

$$x^2 - 1$$

$$20 - x$$

$$(x - 1)^2 + 6$$

$$\frac{30x}{8}$$

$$2x + 9$$

$$5x - 5$$

In questions **3** to **18**, find the value of the expressions given that $a = 5$, $b = -3$, $c = 2$

3 $a + b$

4 c^2

5 b^2

6 $c - b$

7 $2a + 1$

8 $c + b$

9 $4(a - b)$

10 $b^2 + 7$

11 $\dfrac{4b}{c}$

12 $\dfrac{3a + 3}{2b}$

13 $4b - 1$

14 bc

15 $\dfrac{5c - 5b}{a}$

16 abc

17 $a(2c + b)$

18 $3ab$

19 If $n = -2$, which expression has the larger value and by how much?

$$5n - n \quad \text{or} \quad 2(4n + 3)$$

20 Given that $w = -5$ and $x = 9$, find the value of each of the following expressions.

a $x - w$ **b** $x^2 + w$ **c** $4(w + x)$ **d** xw **e** $2w + x$

f $w^2 + 3$ **g** $x(3x + w)$ **h** $\dfrac{10x}{w}$ **i** $w(2x - w)$

5.3 Interpreting and sketching real-life graphs

HWK 1M   **Main Book page 314**

1 Maggie has a peach tree. In the morning she picks a peach and places it on a window ledge in her kitchen. It is a very hot and sunny day.

In the evening she decides to put the peach in her freezer.

Sketch a graph to show the temperature of the peach during the day.

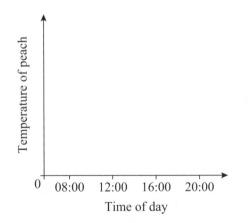

2 The cost of making a telephone call depends on the duration of the call, as shown below.

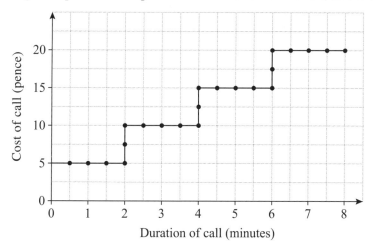

a How much is a call lasting 1 minute?

b How much is a call lasting 1 minute 30 seconds?

c How much is a call lasting 5 minutes?

d How much is a call lasting 6 minutes 30 seconds?

e How much is a call lasting 2 minutes 10 seconds?

f How much is a call lasting 4 minutes 27 seconds?

g What is the minimum charge for a call?

h A call costing 15p is between ___ minutes and ___ minutes in duration. Fill in the spaces.

3

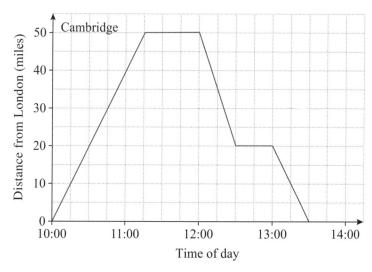

The graph above shows Alan's journey from London to Cambridge.

a When did he arrive at Cambridge?

b How long did he stop at Cambridge?

c When did he arrive back at London?

d Find Alan's speed on this journey from London to Cambridge.

e On his way back to London, Alan stops for half an hour. What is his speed for the final 20 miles of his journey?

4 Sam jumps out of an aeroplane and freefalls before opening a parachute. He then glides to the ground. Sketch a graph to show how quickly Sam heads towards the ground.

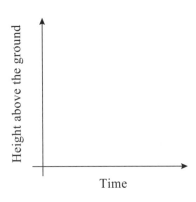

5 On squared paper, draw a vertical axis which goes up to 10 km. Draw a horizontal axis which extends to 5 hours.

Lucy leaves her house and walks for 1 hour at 4 km/h. She then stops at a shop for $\frac{1}{2}$ hour.

She then walks at 6 km/h for $\frac{1}{2}$ hour.

She now walks a further 1 km, which takes her another $\frac{1}{2}$ hour. At this point she walks directly home at a speed of 4 km/h.

Draw a travel graph to show Lucy's journey. When did she get back to her house?

5.4 Ratio and proportion

HWK 1M ———————————————————————— **Main Book page 322**

1 30 : 18 is the same as 5 : 3 because both numbers can be divided by 6

Write these ratios in a more simple form.

a 32 : 12   **b** 20 : 120   **c** 15 : 40   **d** 12 : 18 : 36

e 21 : 35   **f** 54 : 36   **g** 28 : 16 : 32   **h** 18 : 45 : 27

2 There are 90 boys and 70 girls on the school field. Write down the ratio of boys to girls in its simplest form.

3 The Carlton family have three times as many rabbits as dogs. Write down the ratio of rabbits to dogs.

4 The ratio of men to women in a drama group is 5 : 3. If there are 20 men, how many women are there?

5

Write down the ratio of noughts to crosses in its simplest form.

6 If 4 plates cost £28.80, find the cost of 11 plates.

7 3 footballs cost £25.35. Find the cost of 7 footballs.

8 6 boxes of cereal weigh 3480 g. How much will 15 boxes of cereal weigh?

9 Mitchell's heart beats 325 times in 5 minutes. How many times will his heart beat in 4 minutes?

10 Charlie has cartons of juice in a large box. The ratio of orange to apple is 3 : 4. If Charlie has 18 cartons of orange juice, how many cartons of apple juice does he have?

11 Toni has some felt tip pens. The colours red to blue to green are in the ratio of 5 : 2 : 3. If Toni has 12 green pens, how many red pens does she have and how many blue pens does she have?

12

£25 can be exchanged for $36.25
£40 can be exchanged for 44 euros

Use the information above to

a change £40 into dollars

b change £25 into euros.

c Mark buys a meal for $31.90 and Sophie buys a meal for 26.4 euros. Who had the most expensive meal and by how many pounds more expensive was it?

13 The ratio of men to women in a town is 5 : 3. What fraction of these people are women?

14 Margaret and Kelly go out on their bikes one day. The ratio of the distances they travel is 7 : 12. Kelly travels the furthest. If Kelly travels 36 km, how far does Margaret travel?

15 $\frac{2}{5}$ of a group of people prefer shopping at Sureware. Another $\frac{1}{3}$ of these people prefer shopping at Fresho. What proportion of this group of people do not prefer shopping at Sureware or Fresho?

16 Ronnie can buy an Easter egg for £2.99 each or he can buy six Easter eggs for £15. How much money per egg will Ronnie save if he chooses the six egg deal?

17 Sureway supermarket sells 12 chocolate eclairs for £4.08. Dan's deli sells 8 chocolate eclairs for £2.56. Which shop offers the cheaper chocolate eclair and by how much is it cheaper?

HWK 2M ——————————————————————————— Main Book page 324

1 Nick and Beth share a bag of 32 toffees in the ratio 3 : 5. How many toffees does each person get?

2 Some red and blue paint is mixed together in the ratio 7 : 2. If 27 litres of paint are used in total, how much of each colour paint is used?

3 Share each quantity in the ratio given.

   a £800, 3 : 7   **b** £144, 7 : 5   **c** £1500, 3 : 1 : 6

4 In Jennifer's workshop, the ratio of nails to screws is 9 : 5. If there are 450 screws, how many nails are there?

5 The angles in a triangle are in the ratio 4 : 3 : 2. Find the size of the largest angle.

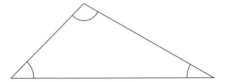

6 Find the smallest share in each of these problems.

   a £48, ratio 5 : 11   **b** 320 kg, ratio 5 : 2 : 3

7 The marks in an exam are given for three different parts in the ratio 11 : 5 : 4. The maximum mark for the exam is 100. Write down the maximum marks which can be awarded for each part of the exam.

8 Josie, Will and Ava have money in the ratio 5:3:8. Ava has £90 more than Will. How much more money does Josie have than Will?

9 Ben sits an exam which has two sections, A and B. Ben's marks on section A and section B are in the ratio 7 : 9. If Ben scores 8 more marks on section B than section A, what is his total score in this exam?

10 Hugo and Ellie's mother gives them £80 in the ratio 7 : 9. Hugo gets the smaller share. Hugo owes Ellie £15 and so he gives her this money.

   Write down the ratio of Hugo's money to Ellie's money now. Write the ratio in its simplest form.

11

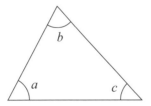

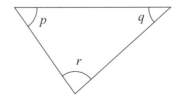

Angles in the triangle above are in the ratio 5 : 4 : 3
Angle b is the middle sized angle.

Angles in the triangle above are in the ratio 3 : 1 : 5. Angle p is the middle sized angle. Angle r is the largest angle.

Find the size of angle r if angle p is equal in size to angle b.

1 Convert each distance below into the suggested metric unit.

    a 720 cm → m   **b** 3900 cm → m   **c** 3000 m → km

    d 17400 m → km **e** 6. km → cm   **f** 260 000 cm → km

2 The scale of a map is 1 : 100 000. The distance between two towns is 8 cm. What is the actual distance in kilometres between the two towns?

3 Find the actual distance in metres between two pylons which are 2 cm apart on a map with the scale 1 : 10 000

4 The length of a field on a map is 1.5 cm. Find the actual length of the field if the map scale is 1 : 40 000

5 Two cities are 6.5 cm apart on a map and the scale of the map is 1 : 2 000 000. What is the actual distance between the two cities?

6 A map has a scale of 1 : 50 000. The distance from Tom's house to the Red Bull pub is 3 cm and the distance from Tom's house to the White Horse pub is 5.5 cm. How many kilometres further from Tom's house is the White Horse pub than the Red Bull pub?

7 Colin and Adele are hiking. They fix their positions and are 12 km from each other. How far is this on a map if the scale is 1 : 200 000?

8 Two ships are 30 km apart from each other. How far is this on a map if the scale is 1 : 50 000?

9 Map A has a scale of 1 : 200 000. Map B has a scale of 1 : 50 000. Two villages are 8 cm apart on map A. How far apart will the two villages be on map B?

10 The distance from Charlie's house to the Blue Bowl pub is 3 cm on a map with a scale of 1 : 200 000. The distance from his house to the Oyster restaurant is 5.5 cm on a map with a scale of 1 : 80 000. Which is closer to Charlie's house and by how much: the Blue Bowl pub or the Oyster restaurant?

5.5 Percentages 2

1 A centre forward scored 20 of his team's 50 goals during one season. What percentage of his team's goals did the centre forward score?

2 Jackson has 120 logs to sell. His neighbour buys 85% of the logs. How many logs does Jackson still have?

3 Which equation below gives the greater answer and by how much?

    (45% of £60)   or   (80% of £40)

4 The test marks of 5 people are shown below. Order the people, starting with the person who got the highest mark.

Ivor	Olivia	Leo	Grace	Oliver
$\dfrac{30}{50}$	$\dfrac{12}{25}$	49%	52%	$\dfrac{11}{20}$

5 Ella earns £460 each week. She is given a pay rise of 5%. How much does Ella now earn each week?

6 A person's heart beats 70 times each minute. During exercise this person's heart rate increases by 30%. How many times each minute does the person's heart beat during exercise?

7 Three items below are in a sale.

Washing machine £450 40% off	Fridge/ freezer £420 35% off	Dishwasher £390 30% off

Which 2 items now cost the same amount of money?

8 A florist has 40 roses to sell. The florist sells 36 roses. What percentage of the roses has been sold?

9 The floor area of Ivy's house is $70\,m^2$. She has an extension built, which increases the floor area by 15%. What is the floor area of Ivy's house now?

10 A builder gives an estimate of £18 000 for a garage conversion. Another builder gives an estimate which is 20% less than the first estimate. How much money would be saved by giving the job to the second builder?

HWK 2M ———————————————————————— **Main Book page 332**

You may use a calculator.

1 A computer costs £617 plus VAT, which is 20%. How much will the computer cost in total?

2 **a** Decrease £48 by 18%   **b** Reduce £512 by 17%
   c Increase £108 by 7%   **d** Increase £350 by 58%

3 A supermarket worker gets a 7% reduction on any shopping bought in the supermarket. How much would £136 of shopping cost the supermarket worker?

4 Write these numbers in order of size, starting with the smallest.

$\dfrac{152}{800}$	0.18	$\dfrac{33}{150}$	0.2	$\dfrac{7}{40}$

5 Willow weighs 53 kg and Jack weighs 59 kg. Who weighs more if Willow's weight increases by 14% and Jack's weight decreases by 2%?

6 Esme buys a flat for £210 000. Two years later she sells the flat and makes a profit of 21%. How much does she sell the flat for?

7 The table shows how many boys and girls in Year 8 in Hatton School study French and Spanish.

	French	Spanish	Total
Boys	62	49	111
Girls	58	73	131
Total	120	122	242

   a What percentage of the girls study Spanish?

   b What percentage of the students are boys?

   c What percentage of the students study French?

8

Store A
£563
+VAT (20%)

Store B
£690
including VAT

The same TV can be bought in store A or store B. Which store is cheaper and by how much?

9 The population of a small country is 2 250 000. The country will struggle if its population is more than 2 500 000

The population increases by 8% during the next 3 years. How many more people will mean the population hits the danger level above?

10 Jethro's gas bill is shown. How much does he have to pay in total?

Gas bill
£188
plus 5% VAT

HWK 3M ──────────────────────────────── **Main Book page 334**

Use a calculator if needed.

1 £3500 is invested at 5% per annum (year) simple interest.

   a How much money is made over 4 years?

   b Find the total amount of money invested after 4 years.

2 £7000 is invested at 8% per annum simple interest.

   a How much money is made over 3 years?

   b Find the total amount of money invested after 3 years.

3 Kaven borrows £5500. He has to pay back the money after 4 years. He is charged 10% per annum simple interest. How much money does Kaven have to pay back in total?

4 Thea borrows £9000 to buy a car. She is charged 7% per annum simple interest. How much will she pay in total if she pays back all the money after 5 years?

5 Find the total amount of money invested after the number of years shown.

	Money invested	Simple interest rate	Number of years
a	£3000	3%	5
b	£85 000	9%	10
c	£920	15%	6
d	£47 000	2%	20

6 Violet invests £12 000 at 3.5% per annum simple interest. Albie invests £14 500 at 3% per annum simple interest. Who makes more interest after 6 years and by how much?

7

Sure Deposit
5.5% per annum simple interest

Roman invests £15 000 in Sure Deposit. Lexi invests £17 500 in Safe Bank. Who will have more money after 10 years and by how much?

Safe Bank
4.25% per annum simple interest

8 Heidi borrows £15 000 at $3\frac{3}{4}$% per annum simple interest. She repays the loan after 9 years. How much will she repay in total?

HWK 4M ———————————————————— **Main Book page 336**

Use a calculator if needed and give all answers to one decimal place.

1 A cereal manufacturer reduces the amount of sugar in a box of cereal from 170 g to 140 g. Work out the percentage decrease in the amount of sugar.

2 A farmer owns 530 hectares of land. The farmer sells off some of the land so the area of the farm is reduced to 360.4 hectares. What is the percentage reduction in the area of the farm?

3 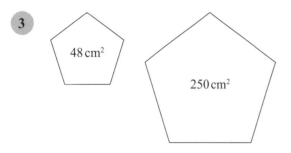 Work out the percentage increase in the area of this regular pentagon.

4 Lexa has £6000 savings. She uses some of the money to buy a £1200 bed. Work out the percentage decrease in her savings.

5 A joiner pays £90 for the wood to make a window frame. The joiner sells the window frame for £148.50. Work out the percentage profit made by the joiner.

6 Malcolm commutes to work each day. The journey takes him 55 minutes. Malcolm gets a new job and the commuting time is 38 minutes. Work out the percentage reduction in the duration of Malcolm's commute.

7 The Jenkins family usually buy 2 small boxes of flakes each week, as shown.

One week they buy one large box only, as shown. Work out the percentage increase in the amount of flakes the Jenkins family have during this week.

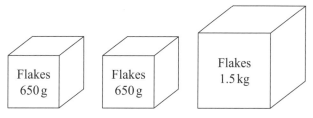

8 Rory takes 72 shots when playing a round of golf on Thursday. On the Friday he plays another round of golf and takes 63 shots. Work out the percentage decrease in the number of shots he takes on Friday compared with Thursday.

9

	Cost price
Football	£6
Hockey sticks	£14

Julia buys 20 footballs and 15 hockey sticks.
She sells 18 of the footballs at £11 each and 12 of the hockey sticks at £35 each.
Work out the overall percentage profit that Julia made.

10 A TV costs £580, including VAT. The price of the TV is increased by £90 then a further 6% of the new price. What is now the overall percentage increase in the cost of the TV from the original £580?

5.6 Statistics review

HWK 1M ———————————————————— **Main Book page 340**

1 The probability of Henry's car breaking down on a journey is 0.003. What is the probability that Henry's car will not break down on a journey?

2

The word JET is removed from the cards above.
Carys then removes one card at random.
What is the probability that this card is a vowel?

3

8	7	1	4	?

The 5 numbers above have a mean average of 6.
What is the value of the final number.

4 The scatter graph below shows the value of a certain type of car and the age of the car.

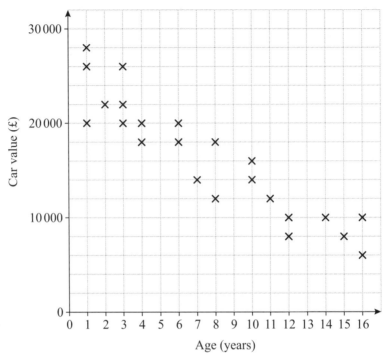

a Describe the correlation.

b How much would you expect a 9-year-old car to be worth?

5 The number of bedrooms in 80 houses is recorded in the table below.

Number of bedrooms	1	2	3	4	5	6
Frequency	7	12	28	25	5	3

a Work out the mean number of bedrooms per house.

b Is the mean higher or lower than the mode for the number of bedrooms per house? Give a reason for your answer.

6 Seven blue balls of diameter 4 cm and 8 red balls of diameter 6 cm are placed in a bag.

One ball is selected. Rishi says that the probability of removing a blue ball is $\frac{7}{15}$. *Explain clearly* why Rishi is not correct.

7 Groups of people in Manchester and Bristol were asked if they prefer going to the cinema, to the theatre or to a restaurant. The results are recorded in the pie charts below.

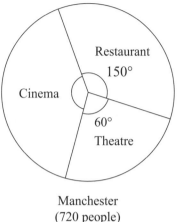
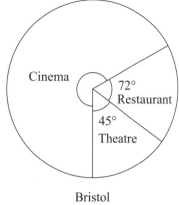

Manchester
(720 people)

Bristol
(640 people)

How many more people from Manchester prefer the theatre compared with the people from Bristol?

8 The stem and leaf diagram shows the weights of a group of people. Which is greater and by how much: the mean or the median?

Stem	Leaf
5	2 7
6	3 3 8
7	2 5 9 9
8	1

Key: 6|3 means 63 kg

UNIT 6

6.1 Measures

HWK 1M ———————————————————————— **Main Book page 359**

> Remember: 1 km = 1000 m   1 kg = 1000 g   1 litre = 1000 ml   and   1 tonne = 1000 kg

Copy and complete

1 7400 m = _____ km

2 40 mm = _____ cm

3 35 cm = _____ m

4 2.5 kg = _____ g

5 4500 ml = _____ litres

6 6.8 km = _____ m

7 320 g = _____ kg

8 6.5 tonnes = _____ kg

9 2.38 m = _____ cm

10 4.2 km = _____ m

11 3.4 litres = _____ ml

12 400 kg = _____ tonnes

13 Simon uses 450 g and 720 g of plain flour when baking. He started with 3 kg of plain flour. How much plain flour has he now got left?

14 Louise pours 740 ml of oil into her car engine from a 3 litre can. How many more times would she be able to pour 740 ml from this can of oil?

15 Which would be worth more?

| Six 165 kg bars of gold | or | One 1 tonne block of gold |

16 Jamie takes 2 teaspoonfuls of medicine. He tells his grandmother that he has taken 500 ml of medicine. Should his grandmother be concerned? Give a reason for your answer.

17 Lena is doing a 5 km run. She runs 2 km 40 m, then 1.6 km.
How much further has she got to run?

18 Henry earns 35p each minute. He works for 12 hours each day, five days a week. How much does he earn in one year? (take one year to be 50 weeks).

19 The total weight of 15 players in a rugby team is 1.6 tonnes. A 112 kg player leaves the field because of injury. What is the total weight of the remaining 14 players?

20 A glass of orange juice contains 85 ml. How many glasses can be filled from a 1.5 litre carton of orange juice?

> ### Converting between metric and imperial units
>
> 1 m ≈ 3 feet   1 kg ≈ 2.2 pounds
> 8 km ≈ 5 miles   1 gallon ≈ 4.5 litres
> 1 litre is just less than 2 pints
> 1 foot = 12 inches   1 yard = 3 feet
> 1 stone = 14 pounds   1 pound = 16 ounces

1 For each pair below, write down which is the larger amount.

a 24 km, 16 miles   **b** 5 feet, 59 inches

c 20 feet, 6 yards   **d** 3 kg, 7 pounds

e 5 gallons, 20 litres   **f** 12 pints, 4 litres

g 90 pounds, 7 stones   **h** 32 miles, 60 km

i 90 litres, 16 gallons   **j** 50 ounces, 4 pounds

2 Luke is 5 feet 6 inches tall and Gwen is 70 inches tall. What is the difference in their heights?

3 Sandeep puts 7 gallons of petrol into his car. He then uses 30 litres during his journey. How many litres of petrol remain from the 7 gallons?

4 Answer 'true' or 'false'.

a An 'average' man's foot is about 24 cm long.

b An 'average' young woman weighs about 126 pounds.

c A can of cola contains about 3 pints.

5 A man weighs 10 stones 3 pounds and a woman weighs 68 kg. Who is heavier and by how much?

6.2 Volume

1 Write down the volume of each object. All the objects are made from centimetre cubes.

a

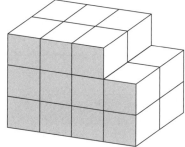

b

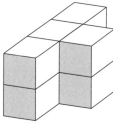

c 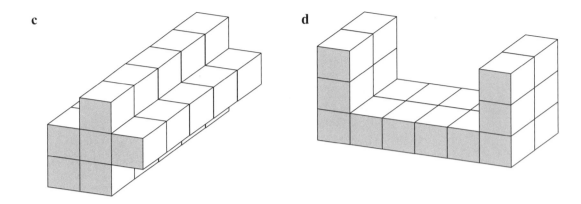 **d**

2 Work out the volume of each cuboid. Give your answer in the correct units.

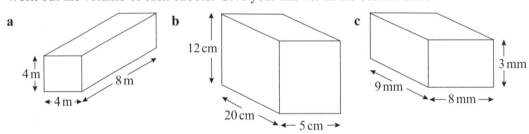

a 4 m, 4 m, 8 m **b** 12 cm, 20 cm, 5 cm **c** 9 mm, 8 mm, 3 mm

3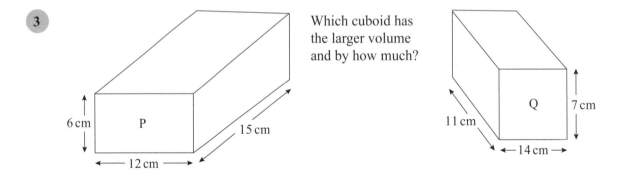

Which cuboid has the larger volume and by how much?

P: 6 cm, 12 cm, 15 cm

Q: 11 cm, 14 cm, 7 cm

4 Find the volume of this solid by splitting it into three cuboids. All lengths are in cm.

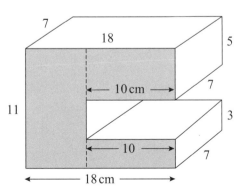

5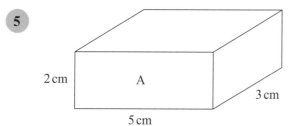

Work out the ratio of the total surface area of cuboid A to the total surface area of cuboid B. Give the answer in its simplest form.

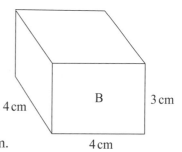

6 Is the volume of this solid greater or less than 1000 cm³? Show all your working out.

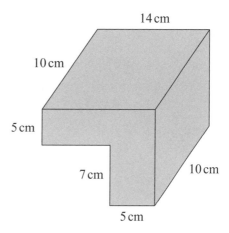

HWK 2M ——————————————————— **Main Book page 366**

1 Each side of a sugar cube is 8 mm. What is the total volume of 50 sugar cubes? Write down if your answer is in mm³ or cm³.

2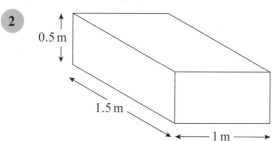

This water tank is full of water. Hannah uses 0.32 m³ of water. What volume of water is left in the tank?

3 Sketch a 5 cm by 3.5 cm by 1.5 cm cuboid, then work out its volume.

4 The entrance to a 300 m tunnel is shown opposite. Work out the volume of the tunnel.

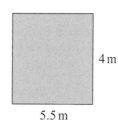

5 Find the length x for each cuboid.

a
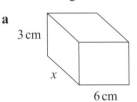
3 cm

x

6 cm

Volume = 90 cm³

b
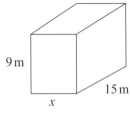
9 m

15 m

x

Volume = 810 m³

c
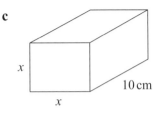
x

10 cm

x

Volume = 490 cm³

6
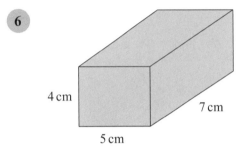

4 cm

7 cm

5 cm

a Draw a *net* for this cuboid.

b Work out the volume of this cuboid.

c Work out the total surface area of this cuboid.

7
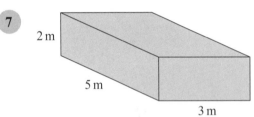

2 m

5 m

3 m

The container on a lorry is shown opposite. Sand is tipped into the lorry at a rate of 0.2 m³ per minute. How long does it take to completely fill the container with sand?

8 How many small cubes of side 0.1 m will fit into a large cube of side 2.4 m?

9
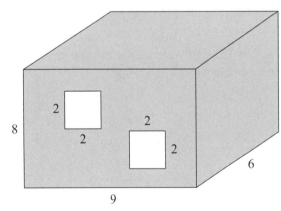

8

2

2

2

2

9

6

A cuboid of metal has two holes drilled right through it as shown. All lengths are in cm. Work out the volume of the remaining metal.

10 Write down an expression for the volume of this cuboid.

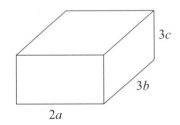

3c

3b

2a

11 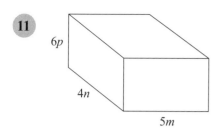 Write down an expression for the difference in the volumes of these two cuboids.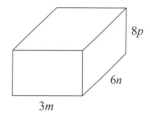

6.3 Drawing three-dimensional objects

HWK 1M ———————————————————— **Main Book page 373**

A *plan view* is looking down on an object from above. In questions **1** to **4**, draw the plan view, the front view and the side view of the object.

1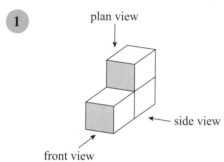

2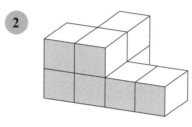

3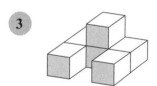

4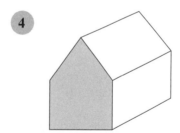

In questions **5** to **8** you are given three views of a shape. Draw each 3-D object (like those shown above).

5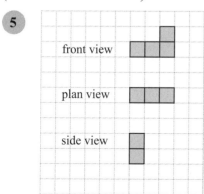

6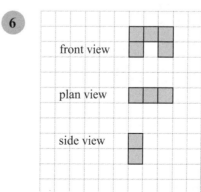

126

7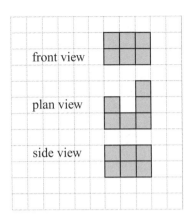

8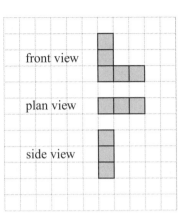

9 Draw a 3-D solid which might have the plan view shown opposite.

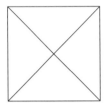

6.4 Algebra review

HWK 1M   **Main Book page 380**

For questions **1** to **12**, use $a = 5$, $b = 2$ and $c = 9$ to find the value of each expression.

1 $3b$

2 ac

3 $5a - 4b$

4 $8c + 3a$

5 $\dfrac{4a}{b}$

6 c^2

7 $c^2 - a^2$

8 $4b + b^2$

9 $\dfrac{10b}{a}$

10 $c^2 - a^2 + b^2$

11 abc

12 $\dfrac{a^2 - c}{b}$

Collect the like terms in questions **13** to **16**.

13 $4m + 6n - 2n + 4m$

14 $3p + 5q + 6p - 2q$

15 $9a + 3b - 4a + 3$

16 $6 + 4x - 2x + 9 - x$

17 Tim has £y. He spends £w on a book and £5 on bus travel. Write down an expression for the money he now has left.

18 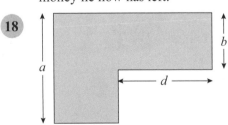 Write down an expression for the total area of this shape.

19 Donna has £*m*. She gives half her money to her son, who then spends £16. Write down an expression for the money her son now has left.

20 Harry has *m* chips. His sister steals 7 of his chips. He drops 2 chips on the floor. He leaves *n* chips on his plate at the end. Write down an expression for how many chips Harry ate.

21 Answer 'true' or 'false'.

a $m \times m = 2m$　　　　　**b** $4m - m = 4$　　　　　**c** $3n + n = 4n$

d $\dfrac{n}{3} = n \div 3$　　　　　**e** $m - 4 = 4 - m$　　　　　**f** $n \times n \times n = n^3$

22 The area *A* of a shape is given by the formula

$$A = 4m + 3n + mn + 8$$

Find the value of *A* when $m = 7$ and $n = 10$

23 Which expression below gives the lowest value if $m = 8$?

| $4m - 9$ | m^2 | $3m - 2$ | $m^2 - 25$ | $(m - 3)^2$ |

24 Which expressions below give the same answer when $n = 9$?

| $n + 7$ | $n^2 + 3$ | $3n - 4$ | $14 - n$ | $2n + 5$ |

25 Simplify

a $n \times m$　　　　　**b** $7 \times m \times m$　　　　　**c** $p \times 8 \times q$

26 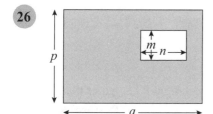　　　Write down an expression for the shaded area.

HWK 2M ──────────────────────────── **Main Book page 382**

Multiply out

1 $5(n + 4)$　　**2** $3(n + 1)$　　**3** $6(n - 7)$　　**4** $3(3n - 2)$　　**5** $6(4n + 5)$

6 $9(4 + 3n)$　　**7** $7(2n + 5)$　　**8** $4(3 + n)$　　**9** $5(3 - 2n)$

Expand (multiply out) the following expressions.

10 $n(m + 4)$　　**11** $a(b + c)$　　**12** $n(y - 9)$　　**13** $x(3 + y)$　　**14** $w(w - 2)$

15 $6(5n + 1)$　　**16** $m(5 + m)$　　**17** $n(n - p)$　　**18** $a(b + a)$

128

19 Write down an expression and simplify it for the area of this rectangle.

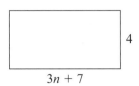

$3n + 7$

4

20 Write down an expression and simplify it for the area of this triangle.

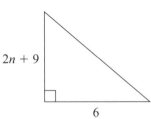

$2n + 9$

6

Remove the brackets and simplify.

1 $2(n + 3) + 4(n + 5)$ **2** $7(a + 4) + 3(a + 6)$ **3** $5(m + 2) + 6(m + 4)$

4 $5(2y + 1) + 4(y + 3)$ **5** $6(2a + 7) + 4(5a + 6)$ **6** $3(3 + 6m) + 5(4m + 9)$

7 $7(2p + 5) + 5(3p + 8)$ **8** $9(4x + 7) + 3(5 + 6x)$

Simplify these expressions by removing the brackets first.

9 $6(a + 4) + 3(a - 5)$ **10** $4(m + 2) - 2(m - 3)$ **11** $5(2n + 3) - 3(3n - 4)$

12 $4(2x + 7) - 3(2x + 3)$ **13** $8(3y + 5) - 4(2y - 5)$ **14** $7(3w + 4) - 5(2w + 5)$

15 $6(5n + 3) + 4(2n - 1)$ **16** $9(7a + 4) - 8(5a - 2)$

17

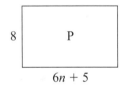

8 P

6n + 5

Q 2

4n + 3

The area of rectangle P is greater than the area of rectangle Q. Write down and simplify an expression for the difference between the areas of the two rectangles.

1 Copy and complete the table for $y = 2x + 1$

x	0	1	2	3	4	5
y				7		
coordinates				(3, 7)		

Draw the graph of $y = 2x + 1$ using 2 cm for 1 unit on the x-axis and 1 cm for 1 unit on the y-axis.

2 Copy and complete the table for $y = 6 - x$

x	0	1	2	3	4	5	6
y			4				
coordinates			(2, 4)				

Draw the graph of $y = 6 - x$ using 1 cm for 1 unit on the x-axis and the y-axis.

3 Use a table of values to draw $y = x^2 + 1$ for x-values from -3 to 3

4 **a** Copy this diagram showing the line $y = 2x + 2$

   b Draw the line $y = 5$

   c Draw the line $x = 2$

   d Write down the coordinates of the point where the line $x = 2$ meets the line $y = 5$

   e Write down the coordinates of the point where the line $x = 2$ meets the line $y = 2x + 2$

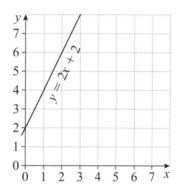

HWK 5M   **Main Book page 385**

In questions **1** to **6** you are given the coordinates of several points on a line. Find the equation of each line.

1

x	1	2	3	4	5
y	5	6	7	8	9

2

x	0	1	2	3	4
y	7	8	9	10	11

3

x	0	1	2	3
y	3	2	1	0

4

x	4	5	6	7	8
y	5	4	3	2	1

5

x	1	2	3	4	5
y	5	10	15	20	25

6

x	1	2	3	4	5
y	6	11	16	21	26

7 Find the equation of the line through

   a A and B

   b A and C

   c B and C

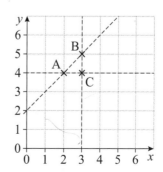

8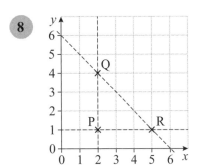

Find the equation of the line through

a P and Q

b P and R

c Q and R

HWK 6M   **Main Book page 387**

Solve the equations.

1 $n - 9 = 13$ **2** $6n = 30$ **3** $5n - 3 = 17$

4 $6n + 9 = 57$ **5** $7 + 4n = 35$ **6** $86 = 9n - 4$

7 $19 = 7n - 16$ **8** $3n + 39 = 75$ **9** $44 = 12 + 8n$

10 If I treble a number n and then subtract 14, the answer is 25. Write down an equation and solve it to find the value of n.

11 Solve

a $\dfrac{n}{5} = 3$ b $\dfrac{n}{7} + 1 = 4$ c $\dfrac{n}{8} - 6 = 2$

d $\dfrac{n}{4} - 3 = 4$ e $\dfrac{n}{9} + 4 = 6$ f $8 = \dfrac{n}{2} + 3$

Solve these equations.

12 $4(n + 3) = 32$ **13** $6(n - 5) = 42$ **14** $5(n - 2) = 30$

15 $7(n - 1) = 70$ **16** $56 = 8(n + 3)$ **17** $27 = 3(2n + 1)$

18 $5(4 + n) = 45$ **19** $3(3n - 2) = 30$ **20** $110 = 10(3 + 4n)$

21 $\boxed{a + a + a + a = 24}$ $\boxed{b - a = 10}$ $\boxed{a + a + b + c = 36}$

Find the value of c.

22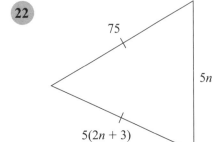

This triangle is isosceles. All measurements are in cm. Write down an equation using n and then work out the actual value of the perimeter of the triangle.

HWK 6E   **Main Book page 388**

Solve the equations.

1 $6x + 7 = 3x + 25$ **2** $8x - 6 = 6x + 2$ **3** $5x - 16 = 2x + 14$

4 $4x + 27 = 2x + 45$ **5** $5x + 45 = 9x - 15$ **6** $7x + 33 = 54 + 4x$

7

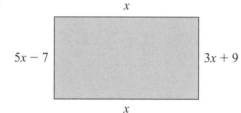

All measurements are in cm.

a Find x.

b Find the actual perimeter of the rectangle.

Now solve these equations.

8 $5(x + 3) = 2(2x + 11)$ **9** $7(x + 6) = 11(2x - 3)$ **10** $4(2x - 3) = 3(2 + 2x)$

11 $3(4x + 1) = 9(2x - 1)$ **12** $8(2x - 7) = 2x$ **13** $6(x + 9) = 3(8 + 3x)$

14 $3(3x + 5) = 29(x - 5)$ **15** $10(9 + 2x) = 33(x - 2)$

HWK 7M   **Main Book page 388**

Simplify and write each answer in index form.

1 $n^5 \times n^3$ **2** $n^3 \times n^2 \times n^3$ **3** $n^5 \times n^3 \times n^3$

4 $\dfrac{n^8}{n^4}$ **5** $n^3 \times n$ **6** $\dfrac{n^6 \times n^4}{n^7}$

7 $\dfrac{n^5 \times n^4}{n}$ **8** $\dfrac{n^8 \times n^4}{n^3 \times n^7}$ **9** $\dfrac{n^{10}}{n^2 \times n^2}$

10 $\dfrac{n^6 \times n^5}{n^3 \times n^2 \times n^3}$ **11** $\dfrac{n^4 \times n^8}{n \times n^5}$ **12** $\dfrac{n^8 \times n}{n^2 \times n^2 \times n^2}$

13   Work out the actual area of this triangle.

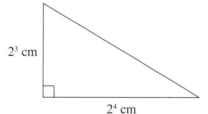

14   Work out $5^2 \times 2^3$

15   If $n^x \times n^4 = n^7$, write down the value of x.

16   If $\dfrac{n^x}{n^4} = n^5$, write down the value of x.

17 Ryan says that $m^3 \times m^2 = m^6$. Explain the mistake that Ryan has made.

18 Write down the actual value of $\dfrac{5^7 \times 5^3 \times 5}{5^2 \times 5^2 \times 5^5}$

19

Write down and simplify an expression for the area of this shape.

m^3

$2\,m^3$

m^3

m^3

20 If $3 \times 3^{2x} = 3^5$, work out the value of x.

6.5 Probability 2

HWK 1M ———————————————————————— **Main Book page 396**

1 The probability of a netball team winning a game is 0.6. What is the probability that the netball team will not win the next game?

2 | H | O | M | E | W | O | R | K |

A card from above is chosen randomly. What is the probability that the letter 'O' is chosen?

3

The needle is spun 75 times.
How many times would you expect
the needle to point to 'win'?

4 A bag contains 6 green balls and 5 yellow balls. One ball is selected at random.
Find the probability of selecting

a a yellow ball   **b** not a yellow ball   **c** a red ball.

5 | S | U | R | E | W | A | Y |

This old supermarket sign is in bad repair. One of the letters drops off.

a What is the probability that a vowel drops off?

b The letter 'E' drops off. If another letter drops off, what is the probability that it will be a vowel?

6 The first thing that Maisie does on a Monday, Tuesday and Wednesday morning is to have a cup of tea. What is the probability that the first thing Maisie will do on Thursday morning is to have a cup of tea?

7 If a dice is rolled 90 times, how many times would you expect it to land on a prime number?

8 A child's sorting game contains the following shapes.

6 squares	4 kites
5 hexagons	8 triangles
10 circles	3 octagons

A shape is chosen at random. Which shape has a probability of $\frac{2}{9}$ of being chosen?

Justify your answer.

9 Emma has the Jack, Queen, King, Ace of Clubs and the Jack, Queen, and King of Hearts. Ben chooses one of her cards then Ada chooses one of her cards.

a If Ben chooses a Queen, what is the probability of Ada choosing a Queen?

b If Ben chooses a Jack, what is the probability of Ada choosing a Queen?

10 The table below shows the probability of Angus choosing particular toppings for a pizza.

ham	mushrooms	pepperoni	black olives	peppers
?	0.1	0.2	0.1	0.15

What is the probability that Angus will choose ham?

HWK 2M   **Main Book page 399**

1 a For lunch, Alana eats pizza or pasta and drinks cola or lemonade. Copy and complete the table below to show all the different lunches she might have.

Food	Drink
pizza	cola
pizza	

b What is the probability that Alana has pasta and cola for her lunch?

2 **a** A mother has 2 children. Copy and complete the table to show if each child is a boy or a girl.

1st child	2nd child
boy	boy

b What is the probability that the mother will have two girls?

3 **a** Ellie throws a coin and a dice. She could get a 'head' and a '5' (H 5). She could get a 'tail' and a '5' (T 5). List the 12 possible outcomes.

b What is the probability that Ellie will get a 'tail' and an odd number?

4 **a** Mindy uses a spinner (with the numbers 1, 2 and 3 on it) and a dice.

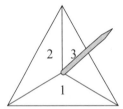 

She could get a '2' with the spinner and a '4' with the dice (2, 4).

She could get a '2' with the spinner and a '5' with the dice (2, 5).
List the 18 possible outcomes.

b What is the probability that she will get an odd number with both the spinner and the dice?

5 **a** 2 dice are thrown. List all possible outcomes (there are 36 ways!).
Copy and complete:

(1, 1)   (2, 1)   (3, 1)   (4, 1)   (5, 1)   (6, 1)

(1, 2)   (2, 2)   (3, 2)   ...   .

(1, 3)   ...   .

...   .

b What is the probability of throwing the same number on each dice?

6 A mother has 3 children. List all the possible outcomes to show if each child is a boy or a girl. What is the probability that all 3 children will be boys?

6.6 Geometry review

1 Calculate the area of each shape. The lengths are in cm.

a

b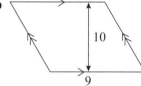

c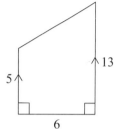

2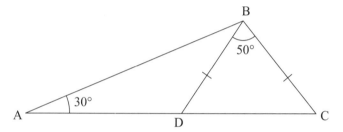

Triangle BCD is isosceles. Work out the value of $A\widehat{B}D$, giving full reasons for your answer.

3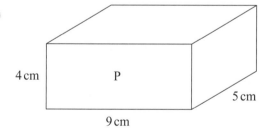

Which cuboid has the greater volume and by how much?

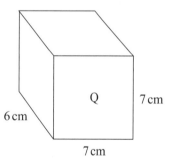

4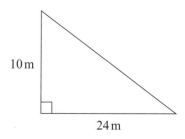

Ali wants to put skirting board completely around the edge of the triangular room shown opposite.
He buys 55 m of skirting board. Will this be enough? Give a reason for your answer.

136

5 Find the shaded area, giving your answer to one decimal place.

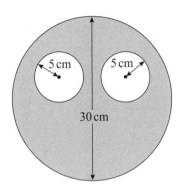

5 cm   5 cm

30 cm

6

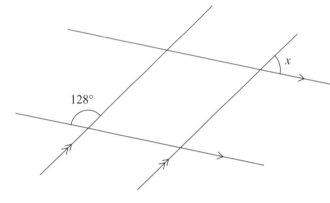

128°

x

Work out the value of angle *x*.

7 Work out the circumference of a circle which has radius 7 cm.
Give the answer to one decimal place.

8 Write down the bearing of A from B.

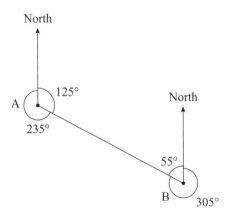

North

125°

A

235°

North

55°

B   305°

9

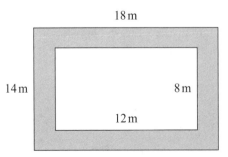

18 m

14 m   8 m

12 m

Work out the shaded area.

10 **a** Copy the diagram opposite.

b Reflect the shape in the line $x = 1$

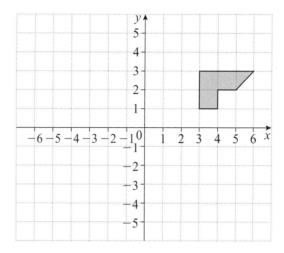

HWK 2M ──────────────────────────────── **Main Book page 406**

1 Work out the total surface
area of this cuboid.

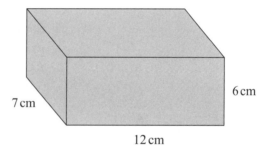

7 cm

6 cm

12 cm

2 A 3.6 m ladder rests against a vertical wall, 2.5 m above the ground.
How far is the bottom of the ladder from the wall?
Give the answer to one decimal place.

3

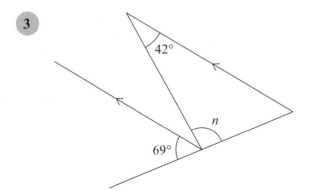

42°

69°

n

Work out the value
of angle n.

4 A circle is removed from a square. Find the shaded area, giving your answer to one decimal place.

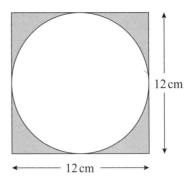

12 cm

12 cm

5

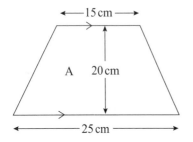

—15 cm—

A   20 cm

—25 cm—

Which shape has the larger area and by how much?

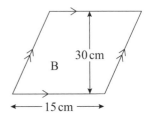

30 cm

B

—15 cm—

6

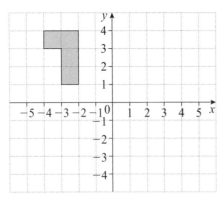

a Copy the diagram opposite.

b Rotate the shape 90° clockwise about (0, 0).

7 **a** A rectangle has a length of 9 cm and a perimeter of 26 cm. Work out the area of the rectangle. (You may find it helpful to draw out a rectangle.)

b A square has the same area as the rectangle. Work out the perimeter of the square.

8 Work out the volume of this solid. All measurements are cm. (Hint: split the solid into cuboids.)

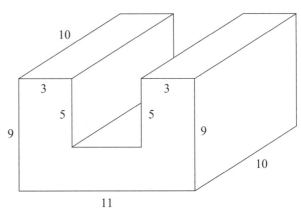

10

3

5

9

3

5

9

10

11

9

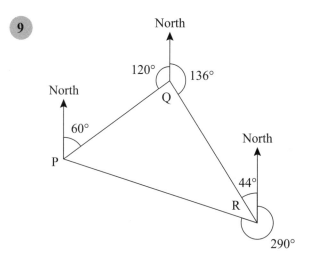

Work out the bearing
of R from P.

10

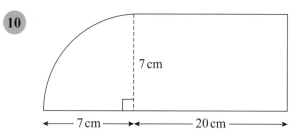

This shape is made from a rectangle and a
quarter circle.

Find the total area of the shape, giving your
answer to one decimal place.